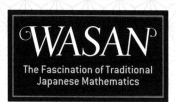

WASAN

The Fascination of Traditional Japanese Mathematics

JAPAN LIBRARY

WASAN

The Fascination of Traditional Japanese Mathematics

Sakurai Susumu

Translated by
Emma Ford, with Gaynor Sekimori

Japan Publishing Industry Foundation for Culture

Note to readers: In this book, long vowels in Japanese words are indicated by the use of macrons, except in commonly known place names and words already adopted into English. Japanese names are written in the conventional Japanese order: family name followed by given name.

Wasan, the Fascination of Traditional Japanese Mathematics
by Sakurai Susumu. Translated by Emma Ford, with Gaynor Sekimori.

Published by
Japan Publishing Industry Foundation for Culture (JPIC)
3-12-3 Kanda-Jinbocho, Chiyoda-ku, Tokyo 101-0051, Japan

First English edition: March 2018

© 2009, 2012 Sakurai Susumu
English translation © 2018 Japan Publishing Industry Foundation for Culture

This book is a translation of *Muchū ni naru! Edo no sūgaku* (Shueisha Inc., 2012) which was originally published under the title of *Edo no sūgaku kyōkasho* by Shueisha International Inc. in 2009.

Book design by Miki Kazuhiko, Ampersand Works
Jacket and cover illustrations by Murotani Noriko

As this book is published primarily to be donated to overseas universities, research institutions, public libraries, and other organizations, commercial publication rights are available. For all enquiries regarding those rights, please contact the publisher of the English edition at the following address: japanlibrary@jpic.or.jp

Printed in Japan
ISBN 978-4-86658-017-3
http://www.jpic.or.jp/japanlibrary/

CONTENTS

 Mathematics Fever 17

CHAPTER Two | *Wasan* enthusiasts and π

CHAPTER Three | *Wasan*, alive today

Exercises

ematics are not aware of their own tradition of *wasan*, and I consider myself fortunate to have had the opportunity to get to know about it. The apparent ignorance of *wasan* certainly is not due to the small number of books about it. Libraries in fact contain a surprisingly large number of books about *wasan* and there are almost too many for anyone interested in *wasan* to choose from. This was certainly my own experience. The world of *wasan* is truly vast. For more than two hundred years spanning from the seventeenth to nineteenth centuries, mathematics fever raged all over Japan, and *wasan*, the mathematics created and developed by Japanese, became broader and deeper.

I realize that it is not easy for people today to understand *wasan*. The original texts are difficult to read because they are written vertically in the cursive style, which is unfamiliar to modern Japanese, who, moreover, are confronted by many idiosyncratic notations and forms. Even when the problems that were solved by people in the Edo period are translated into modern Japanese, they are still not easy to understand. In other words, though there are many works concerning *wasan*, there are few which actually explain it. About three hundred years ago, Japan and Europe were considering the same mathematical problems, even though their languages and cultures were totally different. Encountering *wasan* made me realize that mathematics is a language common to all the countries of the world. The main task for a science navigator is to illuminate difficulties of mathematics and *wasan* thus became my prime focus. I am deeply moved that the book on *wasan* that I wrote initially for Japanese has been translated into English through the efforts of many people, beginning with Gaynor Sekimori. I really appreciate the cooperation I have received from all those involved. There can be no greater pleasure for me than to know that this book will be read not only in Japan, but through translation, all over the world. My hope is that it will bring its readers an understanding of the wonders of Japan and its mathematics.

Sakurai Susumu
Tokyo
December 24, 2017

On the occasion of the publication of the English translation

PREFACE
Seeking the soul of mathematics

In the Edo period (1603–1868), an isolated Japan had its own unique form of mathematics called *wasan*. It had taken a completely different path from Western mathematics but nevertheless rivalled it in its accomplishments. During this period, people all across Japan, from the Shogun to children, practiced mathematics, and what is particularly noteworthy is the advanced level people achieved. The amazing mathematics textbook *Jinkōki*, written by Yoshida Mitsuyoshi in 1627, was used across the country in elementary schools known as *terakoya*, becoming a bestseller that surpassed even popular authors like Ihara Saikaku (1642–1693) and Jippensha Ikku (1765–1831). It was a book that was owned by every family.

Japanese mathematicians like Seki Takakazu (1642–1708) flourished at around the same time as world-renowned mathematicians such as Isaac Newton and Gottfried Leibniz and created one innovative solution after another. Far from being inferior to their European counterparts, they actually surpassed the rest of the world in many respects.

What excited the people of the Edo period about mathematics? The Ichinoseki domain in what is now Iwate Prefecture was a noted center of *wasan*, and even today, there remains a large number of *sangaku*, wooden tablets inscribed with mathematical problems, in temples and shrines in the area. There are also important materials related to *wasan* at the Ichinoseki museum, which I have been to several times. A noted *wasan* mathematician and educator named Chiba Tanehide (1775–1849) was born in the village of Hanaizumi, now part of the modern city of Ichinoseki, and I once visited the farmhouse where he was born, though it is now almost derelict. Although born into a family with a farming background, Chiba excelled at mathematics from childhood. He first studied under Kajiyama Tsugutoshi (1763–1804), the senior counsellor (*karō*) of the domain, and it is said he walked for many tens of kilometers, come rain or snow, to his master's place every day. He was probably typical of many children of his time in the amount of effort he gave to the study of mathematics.

I wanted to understand what spurred them on to such great lengths for the sake of mathematics. It was when I read the words of Takebe Katahiro (1664–1739), Seki's most eminent successor, written in his *Fukyū tetsujutsu* [Inductive Methods] (1722), that I felt I might have touched on part of the solution: "There is good when obeying the soul of mathematics and suffering when not." I do not know of any other mathematician—ancient, modern, Eastern, or Western—who has referred to the "soul" of mathematics. This seemed to beautifully represent in some manner the ideas held by Japanese people regarding mathematics. Saying the "soul" of mathematics implies that a soul exists because we live in a world of mathematics. Takebe's soul resonated with the investigation of the harmony of such a world. This itself was an important discovery for him.

This is when I started to think that the mathematics studied by people in the Edo period and Japanese mathematicians such as Takebe could be called the "way" (dō) of mathematics. Dō usually refers to a spiritual discipline but here it does not mean it needs to be useful in any way. It is simply a mental activity undertaken to improve oneself to the greatest extent possible. Perhaps mathematics is indeed a "way," a way of life for the Japanese people. Takebe's mathematics and words resonate down the generations, as alive now as they were three hundred years ago.

I have written this book to introduce readers to the mathematical world of the Edo period and to explore the mathematical soul distinctive to Japan.

Sakurai Susumu

CHAPTER
One

Mathematics Fever

Today, many students may have tossed their pens down in frustration while studying mathematics. When will I actually apply these concepts? What good will it do for me? Such questions often cross the minds of students who are not interested in studying mathematics. However, even those who dislike mathematics would not deny that at least some of the mathematical concepts are useful; everyone knows that addition and subtraction are essential concepts, and this is borne out by the place of arithmetic in the expression "the three Rs." Certainly before the days of calculators, no one would have imagined getting by without knowing the multiplication table. However, when it comes to topics such as the Pythagorean Theorem, the formula for solving a quadratic equation, or calculus, people tend to ask why they need such knowledge since they can live perfectly well without it.

Even at a primary school level, there is much in mathematics that does not seem essential. Even without knowing the ratio of the circumference of a circle to its diameter is the number π, a circle can be drawn using a compass. Despite this, there would have been very few occasions when a circle would have to be drawn in day-to-day life. Moreover, not many people feel the need to find the area of a trapezoid. In that sense, it can be honestly said that mathematics is not useful. Unless one aspires to work as a professional in the scientific field, it is unlikely that one may need to know the Pythagorean Theorem or calculus.

However, it is also true that just because you do not need something in life, it does not mean there is no point in doing it. For example, music, art, and sports are not particularly useful for most people but few would be of the opinion that there is no point in practicing them. The same goes for puzzles, board games, and video games. If you were to ask someone avidly reading a puzzle book or a book on game strategy how it was useful in their life, they might well question your sanity or might think you were joking.

There was a time in Japan when mathematics was enjoyed as an art or recreation. If you were to travel in a time machine back to the Edo period (1603–1868) and ask the children the practicality of studying arithmetic at a *terakoya*, a private elementary school, they would probably wonder what you were talking about (Fig. 1.1). This thought was not limited to *terakoya*. Though it may be difficult for those who do not like mathematics to believe, mathematics was all the rage throughout Japan at that time.

Figure 1.1 A *terakoya*

Of course, mathematics was also studied to gain knowledge. It was essential for civil engineering and almanac planning, so those who were good at mathematics were valued by the government. It was only natural that the three Rs were taught, even at the *terakoya*, as knowledge essential for life. However, mathematics at that time did not fit a particular framework. Although there were no competitive entrance exams to prepare for, ordinary people grappled with advanced mathematical problems even though they were of no particular use. This is the world of Japanese mathematics (*wasan*) that we introduce in this book.

Sangaku

The *sangaku* ("calculation tablet") can be thought of as symbolizing Japanese mathematics. Wooden votive tablets (*ema*), on which arithmetic problems and solutions were painted, were offered to deities at shrines and temples, around 1,000 of which are still in existence (Fig. 1.2). Some may still be lying undiscovered in someone's storehouse, but many are deposited in small shrines. On seeing them for the first time, modern people might find them peculiar. They contain a series of drawings, made up of complicated shapes combining circles and polygons, making it apparent that they are somehow related to mathematics at first sight. They do not fit the image of a religious institution at all. It is as if a random mathematical equation popped up in the middle of "Romeo and Juliet" or "Gulliver's Travels." However, at that time, the concepts of deities and mathematics co-existed in people's minds and people offered *sangaku* to the deities in thanks that a mathematical problem had been solved.

Although the origin of *sangaku* is unclear, Murase Yoshimasu wrote in his *Sangaku enteiki* [Details about Sangaku] (1681) that they were found at various places in Edo in the mid-seventeenth century and were apparently already in existence in Kyoto and Osaka before then. By the latter half of the seventeenth century,

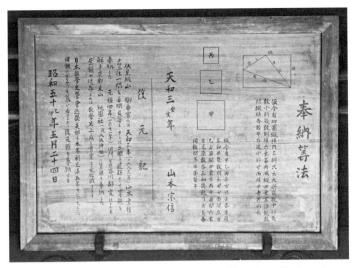

Figure 1.2 Gokō no Miya *sangaku* (restored), Fushimi Ward, Kyoto. Dedicated to Gokō no Miya by Yamamoto Munenobu in 1683.

books containing problems shown on *sangaku* were published, and they had spread to the rest of Japan by the middle of the Edo period. Some say that more than one hundred *sangaku* were offered annually between 1789 and 1831.

Nowadays, *ema*, wooden votive tablets on which people write their wishes, are commonly offered at shrines or temples by students hoping to pass their exams. They ask the deities for help in correctly solving the test questions, but very few of them return

Mathematics Fever

thanks once they have passed the exam. In contrast, people in the Edo period tackled mathematical problems even though there were no exams to be taken and thanked the deities when they managed to solve them, ascribing their success to unseen magical powers. Just as Olympic medalists acknowledge the support of many people and writers and artists attribute their success to divine inspiration when an unexpected creative idea comes to them, people in the Edo period felt that a mathematical problem was not something they could solve on their own. In fact, it was probably similar to sports and art today since it was a form of self-expression. This helps us understand why *sangaku* were dedicated in places where local people gathered. Today, success in an exam means being accepted to a reputable academic institution; however, in the past, people took pride in solving difficult problems.

Some *sangaku* contained only problems. The idea was to present novel and challenging questions in a way that would make people think. In modern-day Japan, it is difficult to imagine that a mathematical problem would be presented in a public place visible to everyone, rather than only in academic books or journals read by professionals. Sometimes, posters on trains advertising cram schools or private lessons show entrance exam problems, but they give the answers in the corner of the advertisement or on the website. However, problems presented on a *sangaku* in the Edo period were challenges: "Solve it, if you can."

Faced with such a challenge, experienced amateurs and professionals in mathematics would try to find the solution and would be determined to be the first one to solve it. When the problem was solved correctly, the solution was announced and a *sangaku* was then presented to the deity. Sometimes, a new problem related to the first problem was added. In this way, mathematics was shared and passed around among the people of a community.

It is unlikely that such a tradition existed anywhere else in the world. Japanese people of the past had a unique mathematical culture that did not end with simple study. Freeman Dyson (1923–), a well-known astrophysicist, has described the originality and creativity of *wasan* in the following way.

> A special kind of geometry was invented and widely practiced in Japan during the centuries when Japan was isolated from Western influences. Japanese geometry is a mixture of art and mathematics.

Early mathematical traces

There is no clear evidence of when mathematical activities started in Japan. However, it is highly likely that some form of arithmetic existed when communities began to form, since having a workable social group requires being able to measure amounts and to keep track of the days with a calendar of some sort. Estimating the crop yield from a particular plot of agricultural land or determining the timing for planting or harvesting based on the movement of the sun or stars requires numbers and calculations.

The Sannai-Maruyama archaeological site in Aomori Prefecture contains the remains of a large village, dating between 3900 BCE and 2300 BCE. One of its largest structures was a large six-pillared building dating from around 2600 BCE. As the name suggests, it consisted of six large pillars, each placed 4.2 m apart. The post holes were 2 m wide and 2 m deep, suggesting that the people who planned them possessed the technology to make accurate measurements. This indicates that arithmetic existed in Japan at least 4,600 years ago. This though was in the form of a practical technique and not an academic system.

The more formal academic study that is better suited to the word "mathematics" is thought to have come to Japan from

China via the Korean Peninsula sometime after the fourth century CE. One of the earliest surviving Chinese mathematical texts, *Jiu zhang suanshu* [Nine Chapters on the Mathematical Art], was produced during the Han dynasty (206 BCE–220 CE). It covered a wide range of topics, such as the measurement of land, multiplication problems involving crops, geometric problems that required finding the lengths of sides from the area, solving simultaneous equations, and even the Pythagorean Theorem. More recent texts were brought into Japan by Japanese envoys during the Sui (581–618) and Tang (618–907) dynasties. These were studied at the Daigakuryō, an educational institution established in the eighth century by the government to train administrators.

In contrast, during the Heian period (794–1185), the focus was more on practical mathematics and mnemonics for memorizing the multiplication table spread widely among aristocrats. The earliest Japanese multiplication table is recorded in *Kuchizusami* [Fun with Learning] by Minamoto no Tamenori (??–1011). However, there are already many examples of wordplay using the multiplication tables in the mid-eighth century *Man'yōshū* [Collection of a Myriad Leaves], so it appears that they had reached Japan before the Heian period.

For example, poem 2542 reads, "Now that we are betrothed,

Mathematics Fever

sharing a pillow of new grasses, how can I endure a single night apart from you?" The word "endure" translates *nikuku*, which is written in the original *man'yōgana* syllabary as 二八十一 (2-81). The play on words here derives from the fact that 2 is pronounced *ni*, while 81 can be expressed as 9 × 9 (*kuku*). Similarly, poem 3242 contains the phrase "at the palace of Kukuri," where again 八十一 (81) represents 9 × 9 (*kuku*). In another example, the number 16 is used to express the sound *shi shi* (literally 4, 4), since 4 × 4 = 16, while 2 repeated is sounded *shi* (4), i.e., 2 × 2 = 4. It is virtually a code.

I am not alone in thinking that there was, among Japanese people in the past, a culture that played with numbers in a witty way.

The *Jinkōki* and the development of *wasan*

Mathematics at this time was not unique to Japan. In China, a new form of mathematics, called *tianyuanshu* (literally, method of the heavenly element), developed through works such as *Suanxue qimeng* [Introduction to Mathematical Science] written by Zhu Shijie in 1299, which dealt with algebra, i.e., finding an unknown number *x*. It was brought to Japan via the Korean

Peninsula at the end of the sixteenth century and had a significant influence on the development of *wasan*. Moreover, arriving around the same time was the *Suanfa tongzong* [General Source of Computational Methods] (1592) by Cheng Dawei (1533–1606), a general arithmetic for using the abacus, employing problems that appeared in the earlier *Jiu zhang suanshu*.

As commercial activities expanded in the sixteenth century, the abacus, also brought from China, came into wide use. One of the earliest arithmetic books to be written in Japan was an abacus textbook, *Sanyōki* [Calculation Manual], by an unknown author, which appeared around 1600. The second mathematical text to appear, *Warizansho* [Book on Division], was written in 1622 by Mōri Shigeyoshi (u.d.), who had opened a school for arithmetic using the abacus in Kyoto and proclaimed himself "the first master of division in the world." He is considered the founder of the lineage of Japanese mathematicians that existed throughout the Edo period, having trained several hundred students, some of whom have left their mark on history. Three of them, Yoshida Mitsuyoshi (1598–1672), Imamura Chishō (u.d.), and Takahara Yoshitane (u.d.), were known as "the three sons of Mōri."

Yoshida Mitsuyoshi, in particular, was a best-selling author who significantly contributed to the development of *wasan*. He was a member of the Suminokura, a wealthy Kyoto merchant family who were involved in finance, overseas trade, and civil engineering. Suminokura Ryōi (1554–1614), Yoshida's grandfather, was known as the "father of water transportation," who constructed canals, making the Oi and Takase rivers more navigable. Yoshida's father was a doctor.

Yoshida became a student of Mōri Shigeyoshi and soon learned everything that he knew. After leaving the school, he acquired a copy of Cheng Dawei's *Suanfa tongzong* through his family's trade connections with China and studied it with his Suminokura relatives, also keen mathematicians. Unlike the *Sanyōki* and Mōri's *Warizansho,* which were essentially abacus texts, the *Suanfa tongzong* began with an explanation of the basics of mathematics, such as numeration systems and the multiplication table. In 1627, just five years after the publication of the *Warizansho*, he wrote the *Jinkōki*, a book about general mathematics not just limited to the use of abacus. It was a best seller throughout the Edo period, a time when more than a thousand books on mathematics were published, far more than in any other country at that time. Interestingly, it sold more copies than literary works by popular authors such as Ihara Saikaku and Jippensha Ikku. Its popularity encouraged explanatory works and unauthorized editions; it is said that over the three-hundred-year period, there were four hundred books with the word *Jinkōki* in their titles. I suspect that every family, both samurai and commoners, owned a copy. It was indeed the "bible" of arithmetic.

Its sales owed not just to its content but also to the fact that it was well organized. The original edition had a decorative binding and contained many pictures; it was a type of book that brings joy by just browsing through it. A comparatively advanced level of plate-making and book-making technology would have been required to put it together. There were not many books like it at that time. Yoshida was able to access the necessary production technology because his family also ran a plate-making business. By combining the understanding of arithmetic that Yoshida had developed himself and the latest publishing technology, *Jinkōki* became a representative book of the Edo period.

This is not all. The book played an important role in developing printing technology in Japan, as a new technology came into being because of it. Having heard how unauthorized versions of the book were making the rounds, Yoshida decided to produce a newly bound edition that no one could imitate. The first edition had been in black and white, but the second edition was issued in four colors. It was then that the *tonbo*-style trim mark was invented.

It is obvious that when you consider the process of producing a four-colored woodblock print, preventing slippage is crucial when one piece of paper is to be printed with a woodblock of different overlapping colors. A trim mark, such as the cross within a circle on the four corners of a galley proof, enables several prints to be aligned exactly. The color edition of *Jinkōki* was produced using this method and is said to have been Japan's first multi-colored printed book. With greater precision achieved, the color printing technology of Japan drew ahead that of China. This technological revolution brought about the birth of the ukiyo-e, known and loved globally. The first multi-colored print was produced in 1765. These beautiful prints could not have been produced without the invention of the trim mark. It is not too much to say, therefore, that Edo culture cannot be described without the mention of *Jinkōki*; the book that triggered the boom in *wasan* was also the catalyst for ukiyo-e.

Incidentally, the title *Jinkōki* was given by Genkō, a senior priest at Tenryūji in Kyoto, at Yoshida's request. As soon as he saw it, Genkō knew that this book would be read and passed down through generations as a book for learning the basics of arithmetic and so named it the "truth that will not change for eternity."

Numeration systems in the *Jinkōki*

Jinkōki, with its attractive appearance and rich content, continued to be read throughout the Edo period as an arithmetic textbook and contributed immeasurably to the Japanese people's love for mathematics at that time, greater than anywhere else in the world.

Before the seventeenth century, many Japanese people could not even do multiplication. However, by the mid-Edo period, a large number of people used the abacus and learned the multiplication tables and how to perform division and so became able to handle both small and large numbers easily. Some people could even work out square, cube, or higher-order roots. The background to this was the popularization of the *Jinkōki*. No other textbook saw such success in spreading the appeal of mathematical problems. It dramatically improved the mathematical sense of the Japanese, and it is likely that the majority of *wasan* scholars who later went on to produce many works had studied this book when they were young.

As might be expected of a textbook used in *terakoya*, the *Jinkōki* starts with the basics, the numeration system, i.e., how to refer to numbers. Japanese numbers increase in units of 1 (*ichi*), 10 (*jū*), 100 (*hyaku*), 1,000 (*sen*), and 10,000 (*man*), up to 10^{12}

(*chō*) and 10^{16} (*kei*), which may appear in finance-related news, but these numbers are less familiar (Fig. 1.3).[1]

Though the numeration system in the *Jinkōki* appears the same as the modern one, it is in fact different. While the *Suanfa tongzong* used a numeration method that is virtually the same as the one used in modern-day Japan, premodern Japan used a numeration method known as *shōjōhō*, where the name changes for each increasing place-value digit. In the *Jinkōki,* although 1 (*ichi*) to 10,000 (*man*) are as they are now, *oku* (today 10^8) represents 100,000 (10^5), *chō* (today 10^{12}) represents 1,000,000 (10^6), *kei* (today 10^{16}) represents 10,000,000 (10^7), and *gai* (10^8) is the equivalent of the modern-day *oku.*

There is also a slight difference between the *Jinkōki* and the *Suanfa tongzong* as to how numbers smaller than one are referred to. The Chinese work has the series *bu* (0.1), *rin* (0.01), *mō* (0.001), *shi* (0.0001), and *kotsu* (0.00001), but for Yoshida, 1 *bu* was 0.01, which was made 0.1 by placing *ryō* in front of *bu.* One *ryō* was a unit of money, a tenth of a large gold coin, so to refer to 0.1 as one *ryō* would be more familiar and easier to remember.

---

1) For information's sake, the numbers above *kei* are *gai, jo, jō, kō, kan, sei, sai, goku, gōgasha, asōgi, nayuta, fukashigi,* and *muryō taisu.* There is a theory that splits the last into *muryō* and *taisu,* but this is a misunderstanding that resulted from a printing error in the *Jinkōki.* Damage between the second and third ideographs of *muryō taisu* appeared as a ruled line making them separate words.

Japanese		English	Numbers
一	いち	*ichi*	10^0
十	じゅう	*jū*	10^1
百	ひゃく	*hyaku*	10^2
千	せん	*sen*	10^3
万	まん	*man*	10^4
億	おく	*oku*	10^8
兆	ちょう	*chō*	10^{12}
京	けい	*kei*	10^{16}
垓	がい	*gai*	10^{20}
秭	じょ	*jo*	10^{24}
穣	じょう	*jō*	10^{28}
溝	こう	*kō*	10^{32}
潤	かん	*kan*	10^{36}
正	せい	*sei*	10^{40}
載	さい	*sai*	10^{44}
極	ごく	*goku*	10^{48}
恒河沙	ごうがしゃ	*gōgasha*	10^{56}
阿僧祇	あそうぎ	*asōgi*	10^{64}
那由多	なゆた	*nayuta*	10^{72}
不可思議	ふかしぎ	*fukashigi*	10^{80}
無量大数	むりょうたいすう	*muryō taisū*	10^{88}

Figure 1.3 Mathematical terms for selected numbers up to 10^{88}

This numeration system is followed by an explanation of units of length, weight, area, and volume, all closely related to daily life. The *Jinkōki* also talks about the use of rulers such as the *kujirajaku* (cloth measure) and *kanejaku* (carpenter's square), as well as the specific gravity of metals such as gold and silver. This knowledge is essential for work in agriculture, industry, and trade.

Multiplication table

The multiplication table appears in Chinese mathematics textbooks but Yoshida arranged it in his own way in the *Jinkōki*. The Chinese multiplication table starts with $9 \times 9 = 81$, but Yoshida changed the order such that it would be memorized from the row of ones. Thus, the *Jinkōki* is the reason modern-day primary school students start reciting the multiplication table from $1 \times 1 = 1$. However, in the revised editions of the *Jinkōki*, the multiplication table was further rearranged and is somewhat different from the modern multiplication table in Japan. Yoshida left out multiples of one and started the mnemonic from the "two times..." row, because multiples of one are unnecessary. Modern-day primary schools faithfully teach the table from the first row but no doubt many pupils think to themselves that it is too simple and there is no need to learn it. Yoshida's decision to omit that row might be more rational than that in modern education. The multiplications to be memorized were thus reduced from 81 to 72. However, that was not all. In a later revised edition, this was cut to 36. Multiplication gives the same answer even if the order is reversed, so if $3 \times 6 = 18$ is memorized, then $6 \times 3 = 18$ is not necessary. That is why Yoshida thought that only half needs to be memorized. This adheres very closely to real life.

In Japan, pupils have been made to blindly memorize all multiplication tables from the one times row to the nine times row, but they are not all used when actually performing mental arithmetic. For example, if three products priced at 80 yen are bought, it would be written as $80 \times 3 = 240$, but people think "three eights are twenty four" and there is no inconvenience at all in not thinking "eight threes are twenty four."

In 1998, revised education guidelines (known as *yutori kyōiku*, unhurried education) were released, which reduced the hours and content of the curriculum in primary schools. A major criticism was that π, the circumference of a circle, was to be calculated as three times the diameter, not the current value of 3.14, given that with the reduction in multiplication in the curriculum, some children were not able to cope. The *Jinkōki*'s way of thinking was the opposite: of first importance was promoting the ability to calculate. There is a broad difference between its idea that it was enough to memorize only half the times tables and reducing the value of π to make calculations even though it is still taught as 3.14. Memorizing just half of the multiplication table is logical, but where is the logic in allowing calculations involving π to be performed at a value of 3? Teaching π as 3.14 and designing a system such that it can be multiplied would be a far more logical solution.

The story of π will appear in detail in the next chapter but teaching it as 3 detracts from the fun (and potential usefulness) of mathematics. In fact, if π is 3, then the circumference would have the same length as the total length of all sides of a hexagon inscribed inside the circle. Surely, anyone can tell instinctively that this is not right. The outer side of a hexagon inscribed within a circle has a length that is three times the diameter of the circle. The fact that the circle is slightly bigger than the hexagon is precisely why π is also slightly larger than 3. Noticing things like this is what plants the seeds of mathematical interest.

Some may think that memorizing just half the multiplication tables is being lazy and not committed to education. However, how easy you can make the calculation is a mathematical skill and is logical. It can even be said that the beauty of mathematics lies in thinking about methods to obtain the correct solution as quickly as possible. For example, the Indian calculation method, which has been gaining popularity in Japan over the past few years, is simply know-how to short-cut complicated calculations.

One such example is a two-digit multiplication method for problems in which the first digits are the same and the sum of the second digits is 10. For example, to calculate 23×27, multiply the first digit of the first number by the number higher than it, i.e., $2 \times 3 = 6$. This is the first digit of the answer. Then, multiply the second digits of the two numbers together, i.e., $3 \times 7 = 21$. We thus get an answer of 621. Similarly, 32×38 is $3 \times 4 = 12$, then $2 \times 8 = 16$, which gives 1,216.

Readers should think for themselves as to how this works. It is with an understanding of such calculations that we find the elegance of mathematics.

A "division table"

The *Jinkōki* did not provide a mnemonic just for multiplication. There is actually a way of memorizing division, too, though it is rarely used these days and I have not memorized it either. However, memorizing it had great significance in the past. You can use an abacus much more quickly if you know the mnemonic for division.

The *Suanfa tongzong*, which Yoshida used as the starting point for his *Jinkōki*, refers to this divisional mnemonic as *jiu-gui* (*kyūki* in Japanese), literally, the "nine returns," since it goes from one to nine. While the division now taught at schools is referred to as *shōjohō*, a method where the division mnemonic used is called *kijohō*. This division system was called in the *Jinkōki* as the "eight calculations" (*hassan*). Since there is no need to memorize division by one, only division by two through nine is considered. Considering though that there can be a remainder with division, a division mnemonic system is not as simple as for multiplication. For example, when 10 is divided by 2, the mnemonic is *ni ichi tensaku no go*, and when 20 divided by 3 it is *san ni roku jūno ni,* but the meaning is not obvious just from this. Here the numbers are lined up in the order of divisor, dividend, quotient, and remainder.

Let us calculate $123{,}456{,}789 \div 2$ according to the example laid out in Fig. 1.4. The basic principle is to divide by two from the highest-place-value digit in order, so the first calculation is $1 \div 2$. Using the mnemonic *ni ichi tensaku no go*, 5 replaces 1 to get 523,456,789. The second stage divides the second digit 2 by 2, and using the mnemonic *nishin no ichi jū* (also pronounced *nicchin no injū*), 2 and 10 are switched and the 1 from the 10 is added to the top 5 to obtain 603,456,789. Next, $3 \div 2$ is calculated separately as $2 \div 2$ and $1 \div 2$, and using the mnemonic *nishin no ichi jū*, 10 is added, and then, using the mnemonic *ni ichi tensaku no go*, 1 is replaced by 5, giving 615,456,789. Placing numbers to lower- and lower-place-value digits using division

123456789÷2
  └→1÷2 (*ni ichi* (2-1) *tensaku no go* (5))→5

523456789
  └→2÷2 (*ni* (2)*shin no ichi jū* (1-10))→10

603456789
  └→2÷2→10 1÷2→5

615456789
  └→2÷2→10 2÷2→10

617056789
  └→2÷2→10 2÷2→10 1÷2→5

617256789
  └→2÷2 2÷2 2÷2

617280789
  └→2÷2 2÷2 2÷2 2÷2

617283909
  └→2÷2 2÷2 2÷2 2÷2 1÷2

617283945

Figure 1.4 Division using the division table

Mathematics Fever

mnemonics in the same way, the final answer of 61,728,394.5 is obtained.

π as 3.16 is divisible by 4

In the *Jinkōki*, the section from Chapter 1, "The Naming of Large Numbers" to Chapter 8 "Multiplication and Division" consists of a general introduction. The main part concerns calculations using an abacus. This is essential for an arithmetic textbook for practical use. It was because it was useful for acquiring basic skills following on from "reading and writing" that the *Jinkōki* continued to be used at *terakoya* over a long period.

Textbooks for abacus had existed prior to the *Jinkōki*, Mōri Shigeyoshi's *Warizansho* being

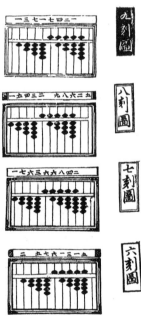

Figure 1.5 Abacus calculation, *Jinkōki*

one of them. There are no major differences between what is taught in the two. However, the *Jinkōki* had a market advantage not seen before: illustrations. The way to move the beads on the abacus was explained through pictures, making it easy for children to understand (Fig. 1.5). Following the explanations of the basics of abacus use, there are a series of calculations related to daily concerns such as rice trading, measuring height and weight, calculating distance, and exchanging gold and silver. An example related to rice trading requires a calculation asking the price of 123 *koku* of rice when the price of 1 *koku* is known. The height of a tree is gauged using a square paper (Fig. 1.6).

> Fold a piece of paper in half to make a rectangular equilateral triangle. Hang a small stone from the corner, as shown in the illustration. Move the triangle so that the top of the tree comes to the extension of its oblique side, and then the distance from that point to the root of the tree is calculated as 7 m. Since the height to the ground is around 0.5 m, the height of the tree would be 7.5 m.

Fig. 1.7 shows the length of the oblique side that changes with the gradient of the roof. Here, when the horizontal length is 1 m, the increasing gradient is recorded for every 0.05 m.

Mathematics Fever

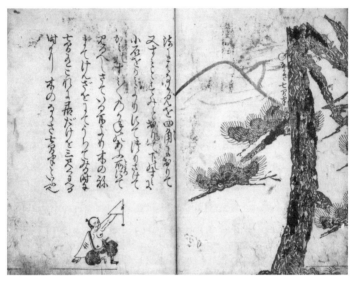

Figure 1.6 Measuring the height of a tree, *Jinkōki*

The highest point, where the height is 1 m, forms a rectangular equilateral triangle. The extension of the gradient at that point is 0.41421 m. If the original 1 m is added to this, the length of the oblique side would be 1.41421 m. We know that the ratio of the three sides of a rectangular equilateral triangle is $1:1:\sqrt{2}$. Thus, the *Jinkōki* expresses the square root of 2, accurate to five decimal places, as 1.41421, bearing in mind the Pythagorean

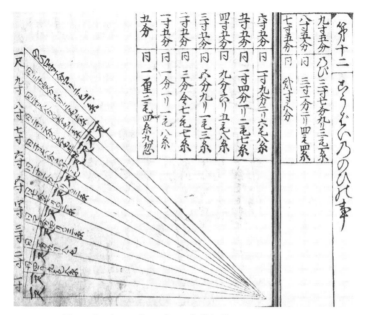

Figure 1.7 Measuring the gradient of a roof, *Jinkōki*

Theorem. Incidentally, $\sqrt{3}$, which is required for calculating the height or the area of a regular triangle, is shown as 1.732 to three decimal places.

By comparison, the ratio of the circumference to the diameter of a circle is approximate. Later, *wasan* mathematicians calculated it to several tens of digits but from its first edition through its various revisions, the *Jinkōki* took π to be 3.16, which continued to be used owing to its practicality, as it is divisible by four and easy to memorize.

Fun calculations (Josephus problem/*mamakodate*)

The *Jinkōki* is closely linked to day-to-day living, with importance placed on practicality. However, in its second half, there is an increased sense of fun. Quiz-based questions, such as the calculation of rats (*nezumi-zan*), (Josephus problem/*mamakodate*), silk thief calculation (*kinunusubito-zan*), calculation of nesting boxes (*ireko-zan*), and rice bale calculation (*tawarasugi-zan*) fill the pages along with humorous illustrations. It is these problems that people are likely to think of first when they hear the word *wasan* (though one of the most famous of the *wasan*, the crane-tortoise calculation, is not featured in the *Jinkōki*). Examples of these problems will be introduced at the end of this book but some are explained below.

The calculation of rats (*nezumi-zan*): The concept behind this can be understood in terms of a pyramid scheme (Fig. 1.8).

A couple of rats give birth to 12 rats, half male and half female, in January. The next month, these 14 rats pair up and each couple gives birth to 12 rats. At this point, there is a total of

98 rats. If these rats continue to give birth at the same pace, how many will there be by the end of the year? The correct answer is 27,682,574,402. Just seeing this answer, children would have been shocked and given a taste of how much fun numbers are. The key to this calculation is that the number of couples increases by seven times each month. Calculating 2×7 to the power of 12, we get the answer given above.

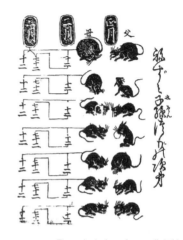

Figure 1.8 The calculation of rats, *Jinkōki*

Josephus problem (*mamakodate*): This problem concerns an inheritance battle between the children of the first wife (dressed in white kimono in the illustration) and those of the current wife (dressed in black kimono) (Fig. 1.9).

A man has 30 children, 15 by his first wife and 15 by his current wife. He decides to choose one child to receive the inheritance. His current wife lines them all up around a pond. He counts his children clockwise from a random child and removes every tenth one, with the remaining child receiving the inheritance. After 14 children are removed, it is realized that all 14 are the children of the first wife. This is a plot hatched by the current wife, who wants one of her children to inherit. The only remaining child of the first wife complains that it is unfair and asks that the counting be started from him the next time. Every tenth child then removed belongs to the current wife, and finally, it is a child from the first wife that remains and so receives the inheritance.

How should the children be lined up to get this result? The *Jinkōki* suggested that the problem be solved using white *go* stones to represent the children of the first wife and black *go* stones to represent those of the current wife. The correct answer is shown in Fig. 1.10. The method is to lay down 30 black stones, replacing each tenth one with a white stone.

Silk thief calculation (*kinunusubito-zan*): Finding out how many thieves stole the silk is based on calculating the surplus or lack. The *Jinkōki* uses the same setting as in the *Suanfa tongzong*, with thieves dividing up their spoils (Fig. 1.11). If they split the silk into 8 *tan* each, there would be 7 *tan* lacking. If they split it into 7 *tan* each, there would be 8 *tan* left. How many thieves were there and what was the amount of silk they stole?

This is easy to solve using an equation, but algebra was not taught in the *Jinkōki*, just as it is not in modern Japanese primary schools. However, it can be solved easily using diagrams, rather than just thinking in terms of numbers. If there are 8 *tan* remaining after each person has received 7 *tan*, there will be 7 *tan* short. This means that 8 + 7 = 15 *tan* would go around for everyone, so there are 15 thieves. The amount of silk stolen is calculated as 8 *tan* × 15 people – 7 *tan* = 113 *tan* (or 7 *tan* × 15 people + 8 *tan* = 113 *tan*). This becomes apparent when the amount of silk and the number of people are shown vertically and horizontally, respectively, on an area chart (For details, see number 6 in the Exercise section).

Figure 1.9 Josephus problem, *Jinkōki*

Calculation of nesting boxes (*ireko-zan*): This refers to placing different sized sets, such as pans, sequentially smaller inside one another. The problem asks, if seven such items can be bought for an equivalent of $21, what

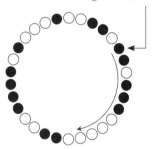

Figure 1.10 Solving the Josephus problem

Figure 1.11 Silk thief calculation, *Jinkōki*

would the smallest cost if the price was the equivalent of 60 cents cheaper for each sequential item?

There are many ways to consider this, but the most interesting is the one that assumes that another of the same set of pans is bought. If the set of pans is a, b, c, d, e, f, and g in ascending order, then the price of a + g, b + f, c + e, and d + d is $21 (= 2,100 cents), making the total cost of two sets 4,200 cents. Therefore, the price of one set is 4,200 ÷ 7 = 600 cents so you can consider the price of one set as a + f = a + (a + 60 × 6) = 2a + 360 = 600, a = 120.

Rice bale calculation (*tawarasugi-zan*): This problem involves piling up rice bales like a pyramid. What is the total number of bales if there are 18 bales at the base, 8 bales at the top, and each row in between contains one bale less than the one below it? The pile of rice bales can be viewed as a trapezium with 18 as the length of the base and 8 as the length of the top. The area just needs to be calculated. There are 11 rows in all (18 down to 8 inclusive), so the solution is $(18 + 8) \times 11 \div 2 = 143$ (Fig. 1.12).

Another problem that appears in the *Jinkōki* concerns the calculation of sharing oil (*aburawake-zan*), one that we still often see in children's puzzle books. How should a barrel containing one *to* (10 *shō*) of oil be divided (5 *shō*) each using a 7 *shō* measure and a 3 *shō* measure. These measures cannot be used to measure 5 *shō* in one go, so the oil has to be moved around a few times. If 2 *shō* can be measured somehow, 3 *shō* can then be added to get 5 *shō*. The key is how to orchestrate this. There are

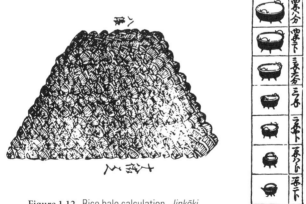

Figure 1.12 Rice bale calculation, *Jinkōki*

many ways of doing this, but the optimal method is the one that involves the fewest steps.

Using the 3 *shō* measure, take out 3 *shō* of oil from the barrel and pour it into the 7 *shō* measure. Repeat this. Now there is 1 *shō* remaining in the 7 *shō* measure. Fill the 7 *shō* measure from the 3 *shō* measure until it is full. 2 *shō* will then remain in the 3 *shō* measure. Drain all the oil in the 7 *shō* measure back into the barrel, and then pour the 2 *shō* contained in the 7 *shō* measure into the 3 *shō* measure. Take another 3 *shō* of oil from the barrel and pour it into the 7 *shō* measure. There is now 5 *shō* in the barrel and 5 *shō* in the 7 *shō* measure.

The game of *go* is played with 361 black and white stones on a 19 × 19 grid board. Puzzles using *go* stones are fun as solving them feels like a workout for the brain. One such puzzle is called *hyakugogen-zan* ("subtracting 105"). The problem is to work out how many *go* stones are there in the pile when taking seven stones at a time several times from the pile leaves two, taking five at a time leaves one, and taking three at a time leaves two. Here, the name of the puzzle itself is a hint. 105 is the least common multiple of 7, 5, and 3. The correct solution is found by finally subtracting 105. But what do we subtract 105 from?

First, multiplying 15 with 2, the number of stones remaining after seven stones have been removed in succession from the total (30). Similarly, multiplying 21 with 1, the number left after removing five stones at a time is 21, and multiplying 70 with 2, the number left after removing three stones at a time is 140. Subtract 105 from the sum of these three numbers (191) as many times as possible. The answer is 86. It is probably not easy to see why these calculations need to be performed but performing the calculations gives the correct answer.

This problem is based on the Chinese remainder theorem. The *Jinkōki* demonstrates it using *go* stones, but in the *Sunzi suanjing* [The Mathematical Classic of Master Sun] (ca. 3rd–5th century CE), it is introduced as a method for guessing another's age. If the remainders are found when the age is divided by 7, 5, and 3, then they can be multiplied by 15, 21, and 70, and added together, followed by subtracting 105 to get the correct age (Fig. 1.13). This is a good party trick (For further details, see number 10 in the Exercise section).

Challenge problems (*idai*)

The *Jinkōki* provided the people of the Edo period with fun calculations such as those seen above, thereby enhancing their mathematical ability. It is no wonder that with a book like this

How to guess someone's age using *hyakugogen-zan*

Let's suppose that when you ask someone to tell you what the remainder is when they divide their age by 3, they respond with "1".

Similarly ask them what remains when dividing it by 5 and 7.

They respond "1" and "4".

Calculate $1 \times 70 + 1 \times 21 + 4 \times 15 = 151$ and subtract 105 as many times as possible.

$151 - 105 = 46$

You guess that their age is 46.

Figure 1.13 Guessing age using the "subtracting 105" method

in every household, mathematics reached a high level of skill and popularity. The *Jinkōki* also deals with problems involving topics such as the extraction of square or cube roots. These can be solved using an abacus. There are still people who can use an abacus and are able to calculate square and cube roots in their heads. It is such a shame that this advanced calculation tool is no longer much used (Fig. 1.14).

However, there was another system within the *Jinkōki* that played a major role in developing the mathematics of the time. In an appendix to the final edition of 1641, when arithmetic had become quite widespread, Yoshida included what are known as

How to calculate √2̄

1 Represent 2 down to six decimal places.

$$\sqrt{2.\,\fbox{00}\,\fbox{00}\,\fbox{00}}$$

2 Seek a for the first number. a is the biggest value such that a × a does not exceed 2. Hence a = 1. Then, write the value of a + a in b, the value of a × a in c, and the value of 2 − c in d. Hence b = 2, c = 1, and d = 1.

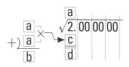

3 Drop down 00. The "2e" × e does not exceed 100 when e = 4. Put the value of "2e" + e in f and the value of "2 e" × e in g. Hence, f = 28 and g = 96. From 100 − g, h = 4.

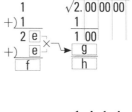

4 In a similar way, "28i" × i does not exceed 400 when i = 1. Seek the rest in a similar manner.

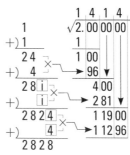

Figure 1.14 Calculating √2̄

"challenge problems" (*idai*), to which no answers were given. He wrote:

> There are people in society who are not that good at mathematics but start a school and teach mathematics to many people. The person being taught will not necessarily know if their teachers have sufficient ability to teach or not. Just being able to calculate quickly using an abacus does not mean having mathematical ability. Here I present twelve problems without showing the solution, so why not test your own teacher's skills?

It is a truth widely acknowledged that whenever something becomes popular, there will be people who will try to make an easy profit from it. It seems that even people without much arithmetic skill were setting up small schools (*juku*) to teach *wasan*. Students must have been concerned whether their teacher could really be trusted and so Yoshida published his problems with no solutions as a litmus test for testing the abilities of people who claimed to be experts at arithmetic.

Let me introduce some of those challenge problems (*idai*). If you can solve them, then you have every right to be confident about your mathematical ability.

(1) When a right-angled triangle with side c as the hypotenuse has sides with lengths a + c = 81 and b + c = 72, find the lengths of a, b, and c. (Fig. 1.15(1))

(2) A frustum in which the circumference of the upper base is 2.5 m, the circumference of the lower base is 5 m with a height of 18 m split into three by volume. What is the height of each? (Fig. 1.15 (2))

(3) 80 pine and 50 Japanese cypress trees cost 2 *kan* 790 *monme* of silver, 120 pine and 40 cedar trees cost 2 *kan* 322 *monme* of silver, 90 cedar and 150 chestnut trees cost 1 *kan* 932 *monme* of silver, and 120 chestnut and 7 Japanese cypress trees cost 419 *monme* of silver. How much does one cypress, chestnut, cedar, and pine cost? (Fig. 1.16 (3))

(4) A circular mansion with a diameter of 100 m is to be split by two parallel bowstrings so that the areas are divided into 2,900 m^2, 2,500 m^2, and 2,500 m^2. Find the lengths of the bowstring and the arrow. (Fig. 1.17(4))

The last question is very difficult. To solve it, you need to solve a quartic equation. It could not have been solved by anyone when it was first published and in fact was too difficult for testing the ability of fake teachers. It would therefore have been a particularly

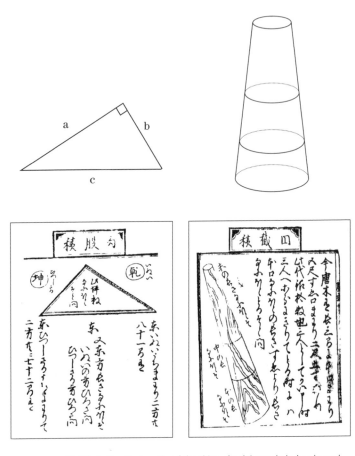

Figure 1.15 *Idai* (1), finding the lengths of the sides of a right-angled triangle, and (2), calculating the height of each section of a frustum

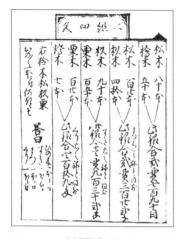

Figure 1.16 *Idai* (3), finding the cost of different varieties of tree

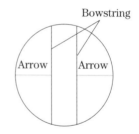

Figure 1.17 *Idai* (4) the problem of the circular mansion

irritating problem for serious teachers, and a shame if someone was marked as a poor teacher for being unable to solve it. Nevertheless, it was because such a difficult question existed that the concept of *idai* started by Yoshida eventually became the power behind raising Japanese standards in mathematics.

Idai were featured frequently in books on arithmetic at the time, not just in the *Jinkōki*. Some mystery novels leave the final solution as an open-ended puzzle in order to let the readers decide it for themselves, and the *idai* in the mathematics books do the same. I am sure that some readers are desperate by now to know the answer to the questions mentioned above.

When *sangaku* contained just the problem, with no solution, many people attempted to solve it, and those who solved it, propounded new ones. The way in which questions and solutions follow on from one another in this way was referred to as *idai keishō* (challenge problems left for posterity). Skilled *wasan* enthusiasts repeated their challenges, and by mutually polishing each other's skills, they raised the mathematics standard of the Edo period by many levels. As a result, *wasan* went beyond the practical world of the *Jinkōki*, which adhered closely to day-to-day needs and became an extremely advanced academic subject. It would be in fact more accurate to say that true *wasan* started at a point after the *Jinkōki*, which was merely something that Yoshida wrote based on the *Suanfa tongzong*. *Wasan* went beyond this and was more advanced than the mathematics of China at the time.

Eighth-order equations and the non-professional

A major influence on *wasan*'s rapid development was the *tianyuanshu* of the *Suanxue qimeng*, mentioned briefly above. Increasingly challenging problems that developed out of the *idai keishō* system could no longer be solved with simple calculation methods using an abacus; algebra was required. *Tianyuanshu* was a method for finding an unknown number (*tianyuan*, "heavenly element"); it is considered as a higher-order equation with one unknown. However, it would not have been solved by writing an equation in the form $x^2 + 2x - 15 = 0$. Instead, instruments called *sangi* and *sanban* were used. They originated in China and may have reached Japan by the seventh century. The *sangi* may have been used during the late sixteenth century cadastral surveys although the abacus had been introduced well before that. It was probably the main calculation tool before the Edo period (Fig. 1.18).

Sangi were small wooden rods around 5 cm in length, something like the *tenbō* used in Mahjong. There were two types, red and black—the red representing a positive number and the black a negative one. The basic approach was to arrange the first five vertically, representing the numbers 1 to 5 (Fig. 1.19). The numbers 6–9 were represented by a horizontal line, which can

Figure 1.18 *Sangi* and *sanban*

be seen as indicating 5, placed over the first four vertical settings (1–4). There are similarities here with Roman numerals.

The *sangi* were arranged on a *sanban*, a board marked with a grid layout, where each location had a specific meaning. Fig. 1.20 shows the equation $x^2 + 2x - 15 = 0$ expressed on a *sanban* in diagrammatic form. The horizontal axis shows the place values; the vertical axis shows the solution, the constant term (in this case, −15), and the coefficients x and x^2.[2] It is difficult to

---

2) The *sanban* comprises columns expressing numbers and rows representing mathematical functions termed as *shō* (solution), *jitsu* (constant), *hō* (coefficient of x), *ren* (coefficient of x^2), etc.

1	2	3	4	5	6	7	8	9	10
丨	丨丨	丨丨丨	丨丨丨丨	丨丨丨丨丨	丅	丅丅	丁丁丁	丁丁丁丁	一
11	**12**	**13**	**14**	**15**	**16**	**17**	**18**	**19**	**20**
一丨	一丨丨	一丨丨丨	一丨丨丨丨	一丨丨丨丨丨	一丅	一丅丅	一丁丁丁	一丁丁丁丁	二
		30	**40**	**50**	**60**	**70**	**80**	**90**	
		≡	三	三	⊥	⊥	⊥	⊥	

Figure 1.19 Placing the *sangi*

	厘	分	一	十	百
	0.01	0.1	1	10	100
商 Answer					
実 Constant			5	1	—
法 Coefficient of x			2		
廉 Coefficient of x^2			1		

Figure 1.20 Equation expressed in diagrammatic form

explain how to solve this equation on a *sanban*. One simple way is shown in Fig. 1.23 so if you are interested, take a look.

This is basically a way to perform calculations using approximations to the unknown number rather than algebraic calculations. There must be many who remember the formula for the solution they learned in secondary school for the case of second-order (quadratic) equations (Fig. 1.21). Even if they do not remember the formula itself, every high-school graduate knows that it exists. This formula was constructed using algebra by rearranging the equation while keeping the unknown number as x. The solution is acquired easily by substituting the coefficients of the equation into that formula. In contrast, solving the equation using *sangi* and *sanban* can be thought of as performing

> **Quadratic Formula**
>
> For $ax^2 + bx + c = 0$,
>
> $$x = \frac{-b \pm \sqrt{b^2 - 4ac}}{2a}$$

Figure 1.21 Formula for the solution of the quadratic equation

ing numerical calculations by putting in numbers that might be nearly right as the unknown numbers, filtering down to obtain the correct solution. Of course, the numbers are not just random guesses. It is a system that allows for approximate values to be found efficiently. Some might think that this is primitive but *sangi* must not be underestimated. The formula for the solution learned in secondary school only works for a second-order equation but with *tianyuanshu*, equations of any order can be solved. For example, a *sangaku* at Oga Shrine in Tsuruoka, Yamagata Prefecture, dating from 1695, actually included a problem of the eighth-order problem and its solution (Fig. 1.22). The problem is $x^8 = 386,637,279,427,098,990,084,096$. It is an incredibly large number. The fact that the correct solution is 888 is, however, humorous.

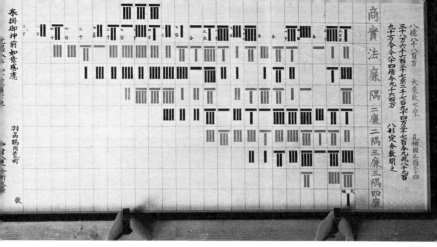

Figure 1.22 Oga Shrine *sangaku*, Tsuruoka, Yamagata Prefecture (restored). Dedicated by Nakamura Hachirobē Masayoshi in 1695.

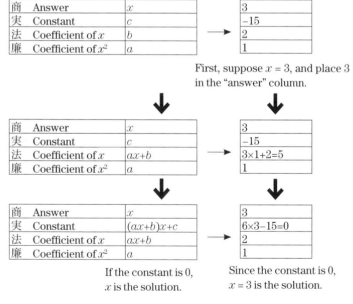

商	Answer	x
実	Constant	c
法	Coefficient of x	b
廉	Coefficient of x^2	a

→

3
−15
2
1

First, suppose $x = 3$, and place 3 in the "answer" column.

商	Answer	x
実	Constant	c
法	Coefficient of x	$ax+b$
廉	Coefficient of x^2	a

→

3
−15
$3×1+2=5$
1

商	Answer	x
実	Constant	$(ax+b)x+c$
法	Coefficient of x	$ax+b$
廉	Coefficient of x^2	a

→

3
$6×3−15=0$
2
1

If the constant is 0, x is the solution.

Since the constant is 0, $x = 3$ is the solution.

Figure 1.23 Calculation using *sangi* and *sanban*

This suggests what an advanced calculation tool the combination of *sangi* and *sanban* was. Modern calculators can calculate eighth powers, but I doubt that many can display 24 digits. It is also an astounding fact that ordinary people were attempting eighth-order equations. It was only in Japan where this was happening at the time. No doubt, if this problem had been given to people in Europe, they would have wondered why they needed to solve it or even what it was. There would not have been any point in even attempting it. Japanese people, on the other hand, were calculating these pointless problems purely out of intellectual interest. The intense sense of achievement they felt on solving them was expressed through the offering of a *sangaku*.

There is nothing that tells the story of how mathematics was established as a hobby more eloquently than *sangaku*.

Seki Takakazu

There is no denying, however, that although even an eighth-order equation can be solved using *sangi* and *sanban*, such a calculation is quite troublesome. Why not use a pen and paper? However, even in China, where both *tianyuanshu* and paper were developed, no such idea was considered. It was Seki Takakazu (1640?–

1708) who developed a way to write down on paper calculations using equations performed on *sangi* and *sanban* (Fig. 1.24).

A major point of difficulty with *tianyuanshu*, which uses *sangi* and *sanban*, was that it could only solve an equation with one unknown (an equation containing only *x*). Once we start to handle harder questions, i.e., equations using several variables such as *y* or *z*, Chinese methods do not suffice. This was made clear as the *idai keishō* system progressed.

The *Kokon sanpōki* [Old and New Mathematics], written by Sawaguchi Kazuyuki in 1671, presented 15 *idai* at the end of the book. They were all problems requiring the use of multivariate equations and thus, could not be solved using the Chinese *tianyuanshu*. Sawaguchi left it to *wasan* enthusiasts to come

up with the answers and Seki Takakazu gave solutions to all of the *idai* in his *Hatsubi sanpō* [Detailed Mathematics] of 1674. In the method he used, there was a notation called *bōshohō*, i.e., the "point counting method" (Fig. 1.25). He enabled equations with several variables to be solved by introducing a way

Figure 1.24 Seki Takakazu (collection of Ichinoseki Museum)

Mathematics Fever

Western format	$a+b$	$a-b$	$a\times b$	$a\div b$	$2a-3b$	$a\div(b+c)$
Bōshohō	$\begin{vmatrix} a \\ b \end{vmatrix}$	$\begin{vmatrix} a \\ \diagdown b \end{vmatrix}$	$\vert ab$	$b\vert a$	$\begin{Vmatrix} a \\ b \end{Vmatrix}$	$\begin{matrix} b \\ c \end{matrix}\bigg\vert a$

Figure 1.25 Seki's *bōshohō*

of calculating on paper using alphanumeric characters. In other words, he invented the long-hand calculation, known in Japan as *hissan*. This is probably his greatest achievement, allowing *wasan* to surge ahead of mathematics in China and develop to an advanced form. Not for nothing was he considered a genius by *wasan* enthusiasts.

He was probably born around 1640, perhaps either in what is today Gunma Prefecture or Tokyo, though nothing is definite. It was considered until recently that he was born in 1642 but this seems to have been based on the claim of a historian that he was born the same year as Isaac Newton. It is almost understandable that he wanted to assert a miraculous historical coincidence. Certainly, the *Jinkōki* was already in existence by the time Seki was born, and like many *wasan* enthusiasts, he is said to have started learning mathematics using this book. There are tales of how he solved all the problems in a day or two, but there is no knowing whether this is true. He studied under Takahara Yoshi-tane, a follower of Mōri Shigeyoshi.

Seki served the Tokugawa family in the Kōfu domain as a bureaucrat whose specialty was accounting and became a shogunal retainer when his lord, Tokugawa Ienobu, was adopted by the fifth shogun, Tsunayoshi. While in the time of Mōri Shigeyoshi and Yoshida Mitsuyoshi, *wasan*'s growth centered around Kyoto and Osaka, Edo became its center with the arrival of Seki, who wrote *Hatsubi sanpō* there, establishing his notation system. It was not however as if Seki announced the birth of his long-hand calculation (*hissan*) in a big way in that work, which merely aimed to solve the *idai* from *Kokon sanpōki*. As a result, much of the solving process was omitted, and *bōshohō* did not itself appear. Indeed, there were some who doubted that the solutions were even correct.

In 1685, eleven years after the publication of *Hatsubi sanpō,* Takebe Katahiro, a follower of Seki, wrote a book of solutions called *Hatsubi sanpō endan genkai* [How to Solve *Hatsubi sanpō*], providing proof that his master's solutions were correct. Takebe is not as well-known as Seki but is another of the *wasan* enthusiasts who represent the Edo period, and it was due to him, together with other of Seki's followers, that Seki's work was handed down to the next generation. *Hatsubi sanpō* was the only book that Seki published in his lifetime. Probably more important to him than status or honor was solving the problem right in front of him to explore the world of mathematics in a pure way.

The Bernoulli formula

Several of Seki's papers were never published. Most of what was published was edited by his followers. One of his most important works, *Katsuyō sanpō* [Essential Points of Mathematics], was released in this way in 1712, four years after Seki's death (Fig. 1.26). It included materials that Seki had written in the first half of the 1680s, made public after 30 years. The timing here is significant, for in it appears a law for which he was actually the pioneer. It was presented for the first time outside Japan in 1713 in the *Ars Conjectandi* by the Swiss mathematician, Jacob Bernoulli. Hence, it is known as the Bernoulli formula in the mathematical world, with its accompanying Bernoulli numbers.

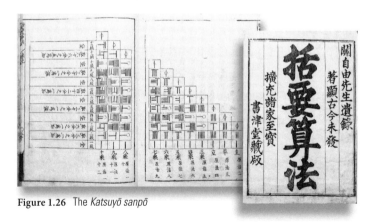

Figure 1.26 The *Katsuyō sanpō*

I am sure that there are many who remember learning the formula for adding together a series of numbers. There are various formulas, including one for the sum of natural numbers: $1 + 2 + 3 + \cdots + n = n(n + 1)/2$, the sum of the squares of natural numbers: $n(n + 1)(2n + 1)/6$, and the sum of cubes of natural numbers: $n(n + 1)/2$ squared. However, Bernoulli's formula is not studied in every high school. It is used for obtaining the sum of a number series. In particular, it is a formula for the sum of a power series. It tends to be confused with another formula, the Bernoulli theorem, which is often used in fluid dynamics. This was discovered by Jacob Bernoulli's nephew Daniel Bernoulli. Incidentally, Daniel's father (Jacob's younger brother), Johann Bernoulli, was also a famous mathematician.

Bernoulli's formula is shown in Fig. 1.27. It can be seen that this corresponds exactly to the rule written in the *Katsuyō sanpō*. Seki achieved it by making steady calculations in a Japan then closed to the rest of the world, unaware of the latest mathematical advances being made in Europe. Seki's followers would not have known that there were mathematicians working on the same subjects as their master on the other side of the world. There was, even so, a tight battle between East and West to make discoveries, paralleling today's rivalry in scientific and technological development. Seki seems to have beaten Europe by a

Mathematics Fever

hairsbreadth. The *Katsuyō sanpō* and *Ars Conjectandi* were published a mere year apart by friends of the authors, both then deceased (Bernoulli 1705, Seki 1708), but

Seki–Bernoulli's Formula

$$\sum_{i=0}^{n} i^k = \sum_{j=0}^{k} {}_k\mathrm{C}_j B_j \frac{n^{k+1-j}}{k+1-j}$$

Seki–Bernoulli Number B_n

(Presented by Seki in 1712, Bernoulli in 1713)

Figure 1.27

it is not clear when the living Seki and Bernoulli discovered the law. Seki may have written it in the early half of the 1680s, but there is no information about Bernoulli. However, since scientists in Western Europe were already competing to make discoveries within various scientific fields, it seems unlikely that anyone would have kept their own discovery to themselves without announcing it. By this token, Bernoulli probably made his discovery just before he died in 1705, which suggests Seki made it first. Consequently, the Bernoulli formula should properly be referred to as the Seki equation. It would be nice at least to acknowledge both people who discovered it at around the same time, by calling it the Seki–Bernoulli formula. I feel that at the very least, the Japanese would be justified in referring to it that way.

"Obeying the soul of mathematics leads to good"

Although no one realized that there was a battle going on with foreign mathematicians, it is not the case that there was no competition within the world of *wasan*. During the Edo period, there were various schools of thought within mathematics. Similar to the "*Iemoto* system" for flower arrangement or tea ceremony, there was a system for masters to pass on their secrets to their students with those who mastered them being declared as having full proficiency. As a consequence, of course, the different schools felt themselves to be in competition with one another. Even though Seki Takakazu's "Seki school" led the world of *wasan*, many other schools existed, including the Saijō school, the Nakanishi school, the Takuma school, the Nakane school, and the Chiba school. There was even a mathematical work written by the head of a particular school that boasted, "Our solutions are shorter than x's school. Therefore, we are more advanced," directly comparing itself to another school. Seeking to solve a problem through as simple a process as possible is typical of a mathematician who wants to solve it in as elegant a way as possible.

This sense of competition sometimes resulted in important discoveries not being publicized. To prevent it from being stolen by another school, a discovery would be passed down to one's own followers as a secret. Such an approach contrasts sharply with that of the modern Western world. This is not the only respect in which *wasan* developed differently from Western mathematics.

Japan's unique mathematical standpoint, which Takebe Katahiro passed down to many of his students, was expressed plainly in his *Fukyū tetsujutsu*: "There is good when obeying the soul of mathematics and suffering when not." "The soul of mathematics"—that seems a very Japanese way of thinking.

People who decry mathematics as not being of any use and who cannot open themselves to how interesting it is probably see it only as an inorganic collection of symbols. All the same, underlying it all, there is a particular kind of "soul" that can only be felt in the world of mathematics. No doubt, the people of the Edo period were able to enjoy mathematics as a hobby because they were able to appreciate that. Modern Japanese can also be expected to sense this "soul." If there is a desire to increase the mathematical ability of society as a whole, innovations must be made for getting to know the soul of mathematics.

The mathematics and arithmetic used in Japanese schools have basically been imported from the Western world. That is why most Japanese people feel that it is a kind of "foreign language." People who are not good at mathematics frequently say that they get a headache when they look at an equation but I cannot help but think that this is similar to a sense of aversion against foreign languages written in an unfamiliar script. Without being aware of it, they are thinking, "This is not a subject for us Japanese." There is no way that this would evoke the sense of a mathematical soul.

However, as we have seen, this did exist in Japan before the introduction of Western mathematics. In the Edo period, mathematics was not just a part of bare existence, as witnessed by the number of mathematics texts being published, more than anywhere else in the world. There were *wasan* enthusiasts such as Seki Takakazu who left a greater mark on the world when compared to some Western mathematicians. Seki achieved more than just the discovery of the Seki–Bernoulli formula. He formulated many theories independently, including algebraic equations, Newton's approximation theorem, maximum and minimum theorems, resultants and determinants, convergence, and calculations involving π. These will be taken up in the next chapter. He did not study mathematics as a Western subject.

Of course, mathematics from China lies at the root of all this. However, Seki went beyond China's mathematics as a result of the discovery of *hissan*, and from then on, a kind of mathematics unique to Japan developed. In some ways, that is how mathematics in Japanese for Japanese people began.

A new notation for Japanese people

In this sense, *bōshohō* as proposed by Seki, wherein any number of unknowns could be used to write equations, can be said to symbolize *wasan*. Modern Japanese people cannot use it, but they do have a mathematical understanding sufficient to design an original style of calculation on paper. We should give that more attention.

In fact, the system for writing numerical equations that is now in use across the world was not established until the twentieth century. Before that the process of writing down proofs had been explained in words. It was France's Nicolas Bourbaki who introduced the style of writing proofs with symbols alone. However, there was no actual individual called Bourbaki. The name is a pseudonym for a fictitious mathematician made up when a group of young mathematicians in France edited an analysis textbook in 1934. Bourbaki wrote dozens of books contributing to and summarizing modern mathematics, which eventually became a model for several countries around the world.

This format aims to assign symbols to various processes to represent them as succinctly as possible, so it was logical on one hand, but it could also be perceived as being difficult to follow. It resembles a code, so many rules first need to be memorized and training is required until one gets used to it. Even some students who studied sciences at university find the format specific to mathematics challenging to come to terms with. No wonder, some laypeople find that it gives them a headache.

However, it is not that such a format itself had always existed, so it is not at all the case that it expresses the true nature of mathematics or anything like that. I cannot think of anything more unfortunate than mathematics being shunned for this reason, for those who get a headache just from looking at a mathematical equation might just not be proficient with the format and might in fact possess considerable mathematical talent. Japanese people liked mathematics so much so that the *Jinkōki* was a bestseller, so it is odd that there are many people in modern Japan who dislike it. Therefore, I think that to bring out the mathematical ability that Japanese people possess, a notation for numerical equations that does not give people headache should be developed. Surely, if Seki Takakazu could do this centuries ago, we, living in the modern world, should also be able to do so.

Western people use only alphanumeric characters but

Wasan Enthusiasts
and π

"Prove that π is greater than 3.05"

Perhaps the advertisements most avidly read by commuters on crowded trains, wherein there is often not even enough room to open a newspaper, are those showing magazine headlines. Reading them is often the best way to pass the time and there may be many commuters who feel they have read the entire article just by reading the headline. The second-most read, in my opinion, although it depends on the person, are advertisements for cram schools.

Only students aspiring to sit exams and their parents are attracted by tag lines that boast about the number of successful exam entrants who qualified to be admitted into the prestigious University of Tokyo. Advertisements that appeal even to those who do not aspire to take entrance exams are the ones that show entrance exam problems. A problem identifying itself as being from a previous year's entrance exam for a particular secondary school really spurs people on to give it some thought, even when noticed very early in the morning. They think they must be able to solve it since it is aimed at primary school students.

Such problems, however, can be surprisingly difficult. Anyone may experience a loss of confidence when they fail to solve a language problem involving *kanji*, let alone a mathematics and science problem.

One advertisement in particular garnered a lot of interest a few years ago. It was for a well-known school specializing in preparing for university entrance examinations and contained a mathematical problem from the 2003 University of Tokyo entrance exam. Such is the prestige of the University of Tokyo that most people would probably give up right then and there, thinking it was beyond their capability. However, it looked very simple and included just a short sentence, which no doubt led some to think they might be able to solve it: "Prove that π is greater than 3.05."

Of course, many people are aware that π is not a number that is a finite decimal such as 3.14. The decimal 3.05 is a subtle number that exists between 3 and 3.14. As described in the previous chapter, it is easy to prove that π is greater than 3. The perimeter of a hexagon inscribed in a circle is three times the diameter, so the circle's circumference is obviously greater than that. This is easy to understand.

However, whether it is greater than 3.05 cannot be determined even if we compare it with a hexagon. We know that π is greater than 3.14; therefore, it has to be greater than 3.05, but how do you prove it? This is exactly how the people of Edo thought when they looked at a *sangaku* displaying an *idai*.

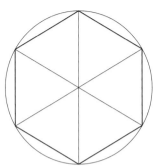

Figure 2.1 Hexagon inscribed in a circle

Although it looks as if it can be easily proven on first sight, many people probably gave up. After all, it was an examination question for the University of Tokyo, so it is hardly likely to have been simple. In fact, it is not so difficult. If you realize that an inscribed regular hexagon can be used to prove that π is larger than 3, then you are already thinking in the right direction toward the correct solution. You need to think of a polygon with a slightly longer perimeter than a regular hexagon and prove that its perimeter is greater than 3.05.

The reason that the perimeter of the regular hexagon inscribed in a circle is three times the diameter is that the six triangles formed by the diagonals of the hexagon are equilateral triangles, as shown in Fig. 2.1. Since the radius is one, the diameter is two, and the length of the perimeter of the inscribed regular hexagon is six, the ratio of the perimeter to the radius is 3 (=

Wasan Enthusiasts and π

$6 \div 2$). Thinking along these lines, using a heptagon as a polygon whose perimeter is slightly longer than that of a regular hexagon is not really suitable because 360° cannot be divided by 7. The calculation would be easier if it can be divided exactly. We will try using an octagon first. If

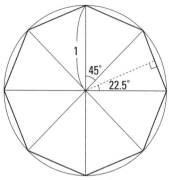

Figure 2.2 Octagon inscribed in a circle

the perimeter is less than 3.05 times the diameter, then we will try it with a dodecagon. Such thinking requires mathematical ability and is the key in solving this problem.

Once you reach this point, you just need to perform the calculations accurately. First, as shown in the figure, construct a right triangle with an angle of 22.5° touching the center of the circle. The perimeter of the regular octagon is 16 times the base of the right triangle. The ratio of the three sides of the right triangle can be calculated using trigonometric functions once the three angles are known (Fig. 2.2). The calculation process is shown in Figure 2.3. There are various other ways of proving it but I suspect that most of the students who arrived at the correct solution used a regular octagon or a regular dodecagon.

If the radius of a circle is 1, the perimeter of an inscribed regular octagon is equal to $8 \times (2 \sin 22.5°) = 16 \sin 22.5°$.

If the "equation for half-angles" in trigonometry

$$\sin^2 \frac{\theta}{2} = \frac{1 - \cos \theta}{2}$$

is used, the perimeter can be written as below.

$$16 \sin 22.5° = 16 \sqrt{\frac{1 - \cos 45°}{2}}$$

If $\cos 45° = \dfrac{\sqrt{2}}{2}$ is substituted into this:

$$16 \sin 22.5° = 16 \sqrt{\frac{1 - \cos 45°}{2}}$$
$$= 16 \sqrt{\frac{1 - \frac{\sqrt{2}}{2}}{2}}$$
$$= 8 \sqrt{2 - \sqrt{2}}$$

The perimeter of the octagon inscribed in a circle is shorter than the circumference; hence,

$$\pi = \frac{\text{circumference}}{\text{diameter}}$$
$$> \frac{\text{perimeter of regular octagon}}{2}$$

is established.

$$\left(8 \frac{\sqrt{2 - \sqrt{2}}}{2} \right)^2 = \left(4\sqrt{2 - \sqrt{2}} \right)^2 = 16(2 - \sqrt{2})$$
$$> 16(2 - 1.414) = 9.376$$
$$> 3.05^2 = 9.3025$$
$$\therefore \quad \pi > 3.05$$

Figure 2.3 Calculating π is greater than 3.05

The history of π

I brought the aforementioned examination question to your attention because I wanted you to get a slight sense of how *wasan* mathematicians during the Edo period might have felt.

Nothing has probably attracted as much attention from mathematicians as π. A major reason for this is that it is more difficult than one would imagine to calculate the length of the circumference of a circle. It was no different in *wasan*. Many Edo period *wasan* mathematicians, including Seki Takakazu, attempted to calculate π. Indeed, π can be said to symbolize how far *wasan* had advanced. The method of calculating it at that time was essentially the same as the way of solving the entrance exam question.

The basic thinking behind calculating π is that the greater the n of a regular n-gon, the closer its perimeter is to the circumference, thereby improving accuracy. However, this idea did not start in the Edo period. In fact, people had been trying since around 2000 BCE to calculate π using regular polygons. In ancient Babylon, 3 + 1/7 or 3 + 1/8 was apparently being used as an approximation to π because the perimeter of a regular hexagon inscribed in a circle was three times the diameter. A few hundred years later in Egypt, an approximation of 256/81 (around

3.1605) is said to have been obtained. However, this did not compare the perimeter of an inscribed regular polygon to that of a circle, but instead was calculated by comparing the respective areas. It was Archimedes in the third century BCE who proved that the value of the circumference divided by the diameter is the same as the area of a circle divided by the radius to the second power. This had been known through experience in ancient Egypt 1500 years earlier. In the fifth century BCE, an attempt was made in Heraclea to obtain an approximation to π by approaching it from above and below, calculating the areas not only of inscribed polygons but also of circumscribed polygons (Fig. 2.4). For example, the perimeter of an inscribed polygon is greater than 3.05 if it is a regular octagon, but the regular octagon cir-

cumscribed in a circle has a perimeter of less than 3.15. Therefore, π would be somewhere in the range 3.05 < π < 3.15. The greater the number of sides of a polygon, the narrower the range of the solution.

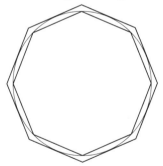

In China, in the second century CE, π was calculated as √10 by comparing it to

Figure 2.4 A regular octagon inscribed in a circle and circumscribed around the circle the perimeter of a square circumscribed in a circle. It would be wonderful if the square root of 10 really was equal to π. It was, in fact, merely an approximation but people at the time might have experienced a Eureka moment, affected by the mystique of the number. Incidentally, $\sqrt{10}$ is approximately 3.162, so it was by no means accurate. However, it was the basis of using 3.16 as π in the *Jinkōki*. Three centuries later, the astronomer Zu Chongzhi (429–500) calculated π precisely to 3.1415926 < π < 3.1415927. A closer value was not calculated in Europe until 1593, more than a thousand years later when a Frenchman named François Viète (1540–1603) worked it out as 3.1415926535 < π < 3.1415926537.

Irrational and transcendental numbers

The decimal expansion of π is never-ending, and thus it is a very difficult concept to grasp. Despite it being a specific constant number that can be expressed using the one symbol, π, there is a mysterious aspect in that it can never be fully calculated, and this aroused the interest of mathematicians. It was not initially known however that π continues indefinitely. It was only in 1761 that the Swiss German mathematician, Johann Heinrich

Lambert (1728–1777) proved that it was not rational. Until that point, calculations were conducted in the expectation of it being a rational number.

A rational number is one that can be expressed as a fraction formed by two integers, and an irrational number is one that cannot be expressed as such a fraction. Of course, there are rational numbers such as 1/3 or 1/7 whose numerators are not divisible by their denominators, so their decimal parts continue indefinitely, but these always start to repeat the same pattern at some point (recurring decimal). In contrast, irrational numbers such as $\sqrt{2}$ or π do not recur. However, although $\sqrt{2}$ and π are similar in that they continue indefinitely without recurring, they are, in fact, different types of numbers. There are two types of irrational numbers. $\sqrt{2}$ and $\sqrt{3}$ are known as algebraic irrational numbers because they are irrational numbers that can be the solutions of equations. To be precise, they can be the solutions of algebraic equations with rational coefficients. To put it simply, $\sqrt{2}$ is the solution of $x^2 - 2 = 0$ and $\sqrt{3}$ is the solution of $x^2 - 3 = 0$. π though is not a solution of any such equation: no algebraic equations have π as a solution. This makes it fundamentally different from $\sqrt{2}$. This type of irrational number is called a "transcendental number," a number that exists, but cannot be expressed as a fraction or the solution of an algebraic equation.

algebraic numbers is not nonsensical—it is a truth that has been proven mathematically.

It is not as though there are not any specific examples. Napier's constant e, the base of natural logarithm, is the best-known transcendental number besides π. It continues indefinitely without repeating any pattern:

$e = 2.718281828459045235360287471352\cdots\cdots\cdots$

We will not discuss here what natural logarithms are as it would become very complicated. It is enough for the reader to be aware that this e emerges every now and then when we express natural phenomena using mathematical formulas. It appears, for example, when the temperature of a pie decreases rapidly when removed from a food warmer in a take-out shop. If the temperature change is shown as a graph with time on the horizontal axis and temperature difference on the vertical axis, an exponential curve dipping to the right can be observed. Temperature changes in the same way once heating stops, whether it be a pie, water in a kettle, or bath water, lowering along an exponential curve from the point when heating ceases. This downward trend can be expressed as an exponential function containing e. When a differential equation representing the exponential curve is solved, *e* appears in the solution (Fig. 2.5). It is this transcendental number that governs the natural phenomenon of hot water cooling down.

This *e* is called Napier's number after the Scottish mathematician John Napier (1550–1617), who conducted research into logarithms. Because *e* was discovered by Leonhard Euler (1707–1783), it is represented as *e*, the first letter of Euler's name. Charles Hermite (1822–1901) proved *e* to be a transcendental number in 1873, whereas Ferdinand von Lindemann (1852–1939) proved π to be one in 1882. Euler's formula that Lindemann used for the proof is perhaps the best-known notion in the mathematical world.

In the equation $e^{i\pi} = -1$, *i* is a so-called "imaginary unit" that is squared to obtain −1. This probably marked the end of the mathematics career of many people at school; it is confusing enough to take the transcendental number *e*, which continues indefinitely, to the power *i*, but Euler's formula further takes that to the power π. In fact, it produces a very simple result, −1. The meaning might not be apparent but it must be obvious that it is somehow amazing.

It has been proven that *e* to the power π is a transcendental number. You might think it obvious that taking a transcendental power of a transcendental number would result in a

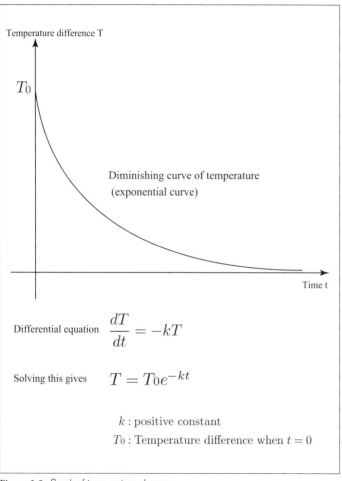

Figure 2.5 Graph of temperature change

transcendental number; however, in the world of mathematics, it is not often easy to prove things properly that are intuitively correct. In fact, many of the hardest problems in mathematics involve proving what everyone knows as intuitively correct or true by experience. This is also the case, for example, with the famous four-color problem. It was suspected for a long time that any map could be colored using only four colors, but it took a long time before it was proven mathematically. No matter how many millions of maps are colored using only four colors, it is difficult to prove that there are no maps that cannot be colored with only four colors.

There was a similar problem regarding transcendental numbers. It is the seventh problem in a list of 23 unsolved problems collated by David Hilbert (1862–1943), a German mathematician, which was presented at the International Congress of Mathematicians in Paris in 1900, much like the *idai* in *wasan*. Problem 7 concerned irrationality and transcendentality: is a^b transcendental for algebraic $a \neq 0$, 1 and irrational for algebraic b? An example of such a number would be 2 to the power $\sqrt{2}$. This problem was independently proven in the affirmative by Alexander Gelfond (1906–1968) and Theodor Schneider (1911–1988) in 1934.

Is π the ultimate "random"?

In any event, transcendental numbers make you appreciate the depth of the world of numbers. The fact that they are hidden in the circle adds to their importance for mathematicians. Mathematicians of all ages and countries have looked at circles and thought hard about them. In some ways, there is nothing that attracts mathematicians as much as a circle. Even though π has been proved to be a transcendental number that continues forever without repeating, people still continue to calculate it despite knowing that it has no end. Such is the extent to which a circle stimulates the human thirst for knowledge.

Computers have calculated π up to ten trillion digits. It is difficult to understand from a normal perspective why one would want to calculate it to that level. It is known that there are trillions and quadrillions of digits to this number, and it is also known that the next digit is always one of ten types, i.e., zero to nine. It would not be strange for some people to think that no matter how many digits are discovered, there would not be any surprising discovery. In reality, however, there is a strong mathematical meaning behind the calculation of π even now. There are still unclear points regarding the true identity of π, and it is important to continue with the calculations in order to understand them.

One such point is whether the arrangement of the numbers of π after the decimal point is random. Nowadays, when more than one trillion digits have been found, π looks to have digits from zero to nine appearing randomly. It is basically the same as the face of a die, i.e., the ten digits appear in equal probabilities. It is not certain however whether that will be the same in the future. Perhaps beyond around ten thousand trillion digits, fewer than nine digits may appear, and beyond that, some digits may not appear at all.

If infinitely continuing digits after the decimal point contain uniformly distributed digits (zero to nine) that appear at the same frequency (this is called a random number series), they are referred to in mathematical circles as normal numbers. It is uncertain how many normal numbers there are among real numbers. In general, most real numbers are thought to be normal numbers, but with transcendental numbers, only a few can be specifically mentioned as such. Although $\sqrt{2}$ and e are both thought of as normal numbers, this has not been verified. It is the same with π. It is suspected to be a normal number, but this too is yet to be proven. In the world of mathematics, empirical rules cannot be used to prove a theory; we cannot say because a number is random down to one trillion digits, surely the rest will be random too. Although going beyond one trillion is huge in the minds of most people, it is a very small series of numbers compared to infinity. Judging this as random is equivalent to thinking that just because a die was thrown once and showed three, this die will roll threes forever. If the digit π could be proven to be random, it would be an incredible discovery.

Human beings cannot generate something that is random. Although there are algorithms that generate random number series, they always contain some type of regularity. For example, music platforms have a function called "random song selection," which randomly determines the next song and plays it, but the order actually contains a sort of routine for that particular program. It can perhaps be described as the order that makes the songs seem to be played randomly.

In contrast, there is a possibility that π is the "ultimate" random number, with no rules or routines at all. Let us suppose, for example, that you spent dozens of years lining up numbers to create a random number series with one trillion digits. If π is a normal number, your random number series is always included somewhere within π. Even if one trillion people made one trillion-digit random number series, all of them would be expected to exist within π.

A circle is a shape unlikely to be related to turbulence. In fact, it can even be said that "circular" is in stark contrast to "turbulent."

There is a possibility that the ultimate random number is contained within it. Surely, this alone is exciting enough to make you want to support the people who are calculating it endlessly.

Muramatsu Shigekiyo and π

After all that let us return to our discussion of *wasan*. The *Jinkōki* calculated the volume of tubs and the like using π as 3.16, but this was because it was a beginner-level textbook that placed importance on it being useful for ordinary people. However, π was not allowed to remain so inconclusive.

As mentioned previously, 3.16 is divisible by four, which is why the *Jinkōki* used it. The quotient $316 \div 4 = 79$ appears frequently. Perhaps people of the time thought of this number whenever they saw something circular. In ordinary standard mathematics texts, being divisible was important and not limited to cases involving π. Even with regard to the extraction of square or cube roots, the *Jinkōki* presents problems such as finding the number that becomes four when squared or 27 when cubed. "Divisible" means that a number can be divided with no remainder, but "non-divisibility" moves beyond this. *Wasan* can be said to have leaped up a level once it began to look for non-divisible numbers, going beyond a state where everything was divisible. It goes without saying that a leading example of a non-divisible number is π.

Muramatsu Shigekiyo (1608–1695) is thought to have been the first to confront π as a non-divisible number. His *Sanso* [Stack of Mathematics] (1663) is the oldest work showing proper calculations involving π. He calculated π using a regular 2^n-sided polygon inscribed in a circle. By using a 32768-gon (2^{15}) he derived a number correct to seven decimal places, 3.1415926. What is fascinating about π is that even though a polygon with 2^3 sides—a regular octagon—can be used to prove that π is greater than 3.05, using a polygon with 2^{15} sides—a regular 32,768-gon—can only reveal seven decimal places. Even so, Muramatsu still deserves praise as a pioneer of π calculation. It seems though that he himself was not certain how many digits of the number he had calculated were correct. If you think about it, this is unavoidable. He wanted to calculate it because it was indeed unknown, with no solution stated anywhere. Muramatsu compared his own results with the π shown in Chinese mathematics texts to be confident that he was correct down to 3.14. Even now, everyone thinks of π as 3.14 but the first Japanese person to calculate this number themself was Muramatsu.

Seki Takakazu and his "acceleration method"

Seki Takakazu (1640?–1708) continued Muramatsu's work. His *Katsuyō sanpō* compiled by his students in 1712, after his death, details his method of calculating π. This research probably dates from the 1680s, also the time he is thought to have discovered the Seki–Bernoulli formula ahead of the rest of the world. It was an era that could almost be called Seki's golden age. In his unpublished *Kaifukudai no hō* [Methods of Solving Secret Questions] (1683) he introduced, for the first time anywhere, the notion of a determinant of a matrix. The first appearance of a determinant in Europe came a decade later, by Gottfried Wilhelm Leibniz (1646–1716), who discovered calculus at around the same time as Isaac Newton. In 1771, Alexandre–Théophile Vandermonde (1735–1796) announced calculations related to the determinant of a matrix, almost a century after Seki.

Wasan mathematicians from Kansai, such as Tanaka Yoshizane (1651–1719) and Izeki Tomotoki (fl. 1690), made similar discoveries regarding the determinant of a matrix several years after Seki, independently of him; such was the fierce competition within *wasan* circles that such discoveries were not necessarily made known outside the particular group. The fact that the determinant was discovered by different mathematicians shows how advanced the level of *wasan* was.

Seki's calculation of π used an inscribed regular polygon as did Muramatsu some twenty years earlier. While Muramatsu used a 2^{15}-sided polygon, Seki used a 2^{17} (131,072)-sided one. This increased the number of sides by 100,000. He obtained a value of π that was correct to ten decimal places: 3.14159265359 ⋯ (the true value of π is 3.1415926535897⋯). He was able to add three further digits (535) to the circle ratio that Muramatsu had found. Given that we have now exceeded one trillion digits, we could say it is only three digits, but at the time, a vast amount of time and effort, as well as ability, was required to get those three digits. Seki's calculation method though was more efficient than that of Muramatsu: when n increased by 1 in an inscribed regular 2^n-sided polygon, the first-order progression of differences in the perimeter becomes an approximately geometric progression (Fig. 2.6). This is what is now referred to as Aitken's

---

Seki Takakazu's π

π = Perimeter of 65536-gon

$+ \dfrac{\text{(Perimeter of 65536-gon − Perimeter of 32768-gon)(Perimeter of 131072-gon − Perimeter of 65536-gon)}}{\text{(Perimeter of 65536-gon − Perimeter of 32768-gon) − (Perimeter of 131072-gon − Perimeter of 65536-gon)}}$

= 3.14159265359⋯

Figure 2.6

acceleration. This was not known outside Japan until 1926 when mathematician Alexander Aitken discovered it, around two hundred years after the *Katsuyō sanpō*.

Incidentally, *wasan* expressed π as a rational number (fraction), and each had a name.

$3/1 = 3$ (*kohō*)
$22/7 = 3.142857142$ (*mitsuritsu* or *yakuritsu*)
$25/8 = 3.125$ (*chijutsu*)
$63/20 = 3.15$ (*tōryōhō*)
$79/25 = 3.16$ (*wakohō*)
$142/45 = 3.155555$ (*rikusekiritsu*)
$157/50 = 3.14$ (*kijutsu*)

Seki's $355/113 = 3.14159292$ is referred to as "circle ratio" or "fixed rate." Of these, it is 22/7 that is best known as an approximation of π, as calculated by Archimedes. For this reason, July 22 is referred to as Pi Approximation Day. In China, Pi Approximation Day is celebrated on December 21 (22 in a leap year) because it is the 355th day from New Year's Day. This was chosen because the Chinese mathematician Zu Chongzhi (429–500) calculated the same approximation as Seki of 355/113. April 26 or November 10 could also be considered as Pi Approximation

Day. The former is the date when the ratio of the total length of the Earth's revolution to the distance moved from New Year's Day to that day, and the latter is the 314th day after the New Year. Of course, Pi Day itself is celebrated on March 14 in many countries because 3/14 is March 14 in the American month/day notation. Curiously, it is also the birthday of Albert Einstein (1879–1955), who developed the theory of relativity.

Zero and infinity

Some say that Seki Takakazu also discovered calculus. If it were indeed the case that *wasan* mathematicians managed to discover this, as Newton and Leibnitz discovered independently themselves, this would be a source of great pride to Japan. Because Seki discovered various types of theories ahead of Europeans, there are those who believe that he must have managed to discover calculus as well. This however is an overestimation. He did not discover calculus, and there were no such concepts in *wasan* until Western mathematics was introduced to Japan in the Meiji period (1868–1912).

Seki is from the same era as Newton and Leibniz. Seki formulated the concept of determinants before Newton and moreover made many other pioneering achievements, like those we have just mentioned. His ability was the same as or greater than mathematicians in other countries, so why was he unable to discover calculus? The simple reason is that *wasan* did not possess a notion of infinity. Achieving calculus was dependent on the development of a notion of infinity, and this did not happen in Japan.

It was because *wasan* did not consider zero that there were no theories of infinity. *Wasan* did have ideographs such as 合 or 下 to represent a number equivalent to zero, but these were simply for place holding; *wasan* did not consider the concept of zero itself. There was no zero, so there was no infinity, and thus, no calculus. All the same, it is undeniable that *wasan* mathematicians, led by Seki, were conducting research that was closing in on calculus. For example, *tekijinhō*, a method for handling problems dealing with maximum and minimum, is like differentiation and the method for calculating volumes or areas by dividing a figure into finer shapes is almost integration. There was however no method in *wasan* for considering a function in a graph format as in the West, and *wasan* mathematicians, focusing on the areas and volumes of shapes, could not move further. Another determining factor was that there was no concept of algebra in *wasan* and algebra rather than numbers has to be used for calculus.

Takebe Katahiro

Despite the fact that *wasan* lacked theories about infinity, preventing the discovery of calculus, it produced a formula for infinite series expansion, which is conventionally based on the premise of calculus. Takebe Katahiro (1664–1739), a famous disciple of Seki Takakazu, derived this formula knowing nothing of calculus. Takebe has perhaps been overshadowed by Seki but some consider him even greater than his master. Succeeding Seki, he conducted extremely innovative research and made major contributions to the development and distribution of *wasan*. His importance is apparent from the fact that the Mathematical Society of Japan still continues to give out the Takebe Prize as well as the Seki Prize. He is a brilliant and significant figure in the history of Japanese mathematics.

Takebe was born in 1664 and was dedicated to mathematics from a young age. He read everything from the *Jinkōki* to the *Kokon sanpōki*, as well as Seki's *Hatsubi sanpō*. He became a disciple of Seki at the age of only 13, along with his older brother Kataakira (1661–1716). He produced his first work, *Kenki sanpō* [Profound Study of Mathematics] in 1683, when he was twenty. It was written as a counter-attack on criticism his master had received. As we have seen, Seki wrote *Hatsubi sanpō* in response to the *idai* in Sawaguchi Kazuyuki's *Kokon sanpōki* but did not show the process by which he achieved the correct solution. This led many to doubt his accuracy and his most violent critic was a *wasan* mathematician named Saji Kazuhira, who attacked *Hatsubi sanpō* in his *Sanpō nyūmon* [Introduction to Mathematics] of 1681. No doubt Takebe was overcome with righteous indignation that the work of his master was not appreciated. He pointed out Saji's mistake in the *Kenki sanpō* and attempted to rectify it.

Two years later, in 1685, he wrote *Hatsubi sanpō endan genkai* [Notes on the *Hatsubi sanpō*], which allowed Seki's mathematics to be understood correctly and to spread throughout *wasan* circles. It was thus due to the devoted support of Takebe that Seki's theories became so influential. He worked with Seki himself and with his brother Kataakira to develop those theories in the *Taisei sankei* [Comprehensive Manual of Mathematics] in 20 volumes, finally completed in 1710, two years after Seki's death.

If Takebe had done nothing but attack Seki's opponents and help spread his work, he would have been nothing but an unsung hero who was not particularly innovative. Certainly no modern mathematician would be happy to receive the Takebe prize, if one should even exist. However, many of his achievements clearly surpassed those of Seki, in particular the calculation of π. Seki had calculated it accurately to ten decimal places, but Takebe did so to 41.

Muramatsu Shigekiyo had calculated π to seven decimal places using a regular 32,768 (2^{15})-sided polygon and Seki extended this by just three digits using a 131,072 (2^{17})-sided polygon. What size polygon did Takebe then use to extend this by more than 30 digits? Many might think that it had several million sides. Unexpectedly, though, Takebe used a polygon smaller than that used by Seki and one with fewer corners than that used by Muramatsu, a regular 1,024 (2^{10})-sided polygon. This in itself did not however make the calculation possible.

In principle, the value of π can be calculated if addition, subtraction, multiplication, division, and calculation of a square root are known. This would not be very efficient though, and increasing the number of decimal places would be difficult. Seki had surpassed Muramatsu by determining π by what he called *zōyakujutsu*, a method based on a geometric series. This is none other than Aitken's acceleration. Takabe, aiming even higher, discovered a different method, which he refers to in his *Tetsujutsu sankei* [Mathematical Treatise on the Technique of Linkage] of 1722 as *ruihen zōyakujutsu* (a method of successive accelerated approximation). It was this that allowed him to calculate π to 41 decimal places from only ten data points

(Fig. 2.7). What Takebe discovered and used for the calculation of π is known in modern mathematical circles as the Richardson extrapolation, introduced by Lewis Fry Richardson (1881–1953) around 1910. If *Tetsujutsu sankei* had been translated into other languages and read in Western countries at the time, there is no doubt that the Richardson extrapolation would have been known as the Takebe acceleration method.

This is the formula for the infinite series expansion described earlier. It is in fact the Taylor expansion of arcsin x, i.e., the inverse trigonometric function of the trigonometric function sin x (Fig. 2.8). Substituting $x = 1/2$ here yields Takebe's formula.

Takebe Katahiro's π

$$\pi = 3\sqrt{1 + \frac{1^2}{3 \cdot 4} + \frac{1^2 \cdot 2^2}{3 \cdot 4 \cdot 5 \cdot 6} + \frac{1^2 \cdot 2^2 \cdot 3^2}{3 \cdot 4 \cdot 5 \cdot 6 \cdot 7 \cdot 8} + \cdots}$$

$$= 3.14159265358979323846264338327950288841971\cdots$$

Figure 2.7

Taylor expansion of arcsin x

$$\frac{1}{2}(\arcsin x)^2 = \frac{1}{2!}x^2 + \frac{2^2 \cdot 4^2}{4!}x^4 + \frac{2^2 \cdot 4^2 \cdot 6^2}{8!}x^8 + \cdots$$

Figure 2.8

The Basel problem

Leonhard Euler is famous for his research in infinite series. Probably anyone can solve this problem of an infinite series in its most basic form: $1 + 2 + 3 + 4 + 5 + 6 + 7 \cdots = ?$ The answer is the sum of all natural numbers increasing by one at a time and is, of course, infinity. An infinite series is the sum of an infinite number of terms such as this. The fact that the solution is infinite is described in mathematics by saying that the series diverges. I am sure there are some who think that if we add things together infinitely, the answer should be infinite, so that all infinite series should diverge. However, things do not work out as we expect in the real world. It is not necessarily the case that the sum of an infinite number of additions is infinite. This can be shown, for example, via the following addition of the geometric progression $1/2 + 1/4 + 1/8 + 1/16 + 1/32 + \cdots = ?$ Here, one half of the previous number is added indefinitely. At first sight, the solution might seem to be infinite. The solution, in fact, is finite; it is simply 1. It might seem bizarre that adding together positive numbers indefinitely results in one, but this can be understood if you refer to Fig. 2.9, wherein a square with an area one is repeatedly divided by half.

This is akin to repeatedly folding a square of paper in half.

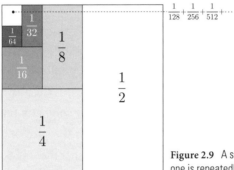

$\frac{1}{128} + \frac{1}{256} + \frac{1}{512} + \cdots$

Figure 2.9 A square with an area of one is repeatedly divided by half

Although in reality it is not possible, it can in theory continue to be folded over and over indefinitely. The geometric progression shown above is equivalent to adding the area each time the paper is folded. The total will never exceed the area of the square and so must ultimately be one. The fact that the solution to this is finite is expressed by saying that the series converges.

Now, does the following infinite series diverge or converge?

$$1 + 1/2 + 1/3 + 1/4 + 1/5 + \cdots = ?$$

This is the sum of the reciprocals of the natural numbers and the solution is infinite. It can be proven by comparing the following equations.

A= 1/1 + 1/2 + (1/3 + 1/4) + (1/5 + 1/6 +1/7/+1/8) + ⋯

B = 1/1+ 1/2 + (1/4 + 1/4) + (1/8 + 1/8 + 1/8 + 1/8) + ⋯

A is the same as the previous problem. B is 1/1 + 1/2 + 1/2 + 1/2 + ⋯ when the numbers inside the brackets are added, so clearly, the solution is infinite. What is inside the brackets in A is always bigger than what is inside the corresponding brackets in B and therefore A is bigger than B, which is infinite. Being bigger than infinite, A is also infinite.

Jacob Bernoulli discovered the formula for the sum of exponential series at around the same time as Seki, who proved that this infinite series diverges. After solving this problem, Bernoulli considered the infinite series, the sum of reciprocals of the squares of the natural numbers. This was however a surprisingly difficult problem and Bernoulli died in 1705 without having solved it.

Euler's work on infinite series

This problem was passed down as the Basel problem to mathematicians like an *idai*, named after the city where Bernoulli lived (Fig. 2.10). Even his younger brother Johann could not solve it.

Figure 2.10 Bernoulli's sum of reciprocals of the squares of the natural numbers.

Leonhard Euler was highly talented and entered the University of Basel when he was thirteen. He developed his mathematical abilities under the tutelage of Johann Bernoulli and was finally able to solve the Basel problem in 1734. The solution apparently surprised even Euler himself. He wrote: "Now, however, quite unexpectedly, I have found an elegant formula for the sum for the infinite series $1 + 1/4 + 1/9 + 1/16 + \cdots$ I have found that six times the sum of this series equals the square of the circumference of a circle whose diameter is 1." This formula feels like it contains the mystery of mathematics. Surely no one would have expected π to appear here, of all places. A circle really is a wondrous shape. In fact, here it is perhaps more spooky than wondrous.

Basel problem

$$\frac{1}{1^2} + \frac{1}{2^2} + \frac{1}{3^2} + \frac{1}{4^2} + \frac{1}{5^2} + \frac{1}{6^2} + \frac{1}{7^2} + \frac{1}{8^2} + \frac{1}{9^2} + \frac{1}{10^2} + \cdots = \ ?$$

Jacob Bernoulli
(1654-1705, Switzerland)

Euler gets there in 1735

$$\frac{1}{1^2} + \frac{1}{2^2} + \frac{1}{3^2} + \frac{1}{4^2} + \frac{1}{5^2} + \frac{1}{6^2} + \frac{1}{7^2} + \frac{1}{8^2} + \frac{1}{9^2} + \frac{1}{10^2} + \cdots = \frac{\pi^2}{6}$$

Leonhard Euler
(1707-1783, Switzerland)

If only my older brother were still alive!

Johann Bernoulli
(1667-1748, Switzerland)

Figure 2.11 Euler's formula

Let us now return to Takebe. In solving the Basel problem in 1735, Euler discovered the same formula for an infinite series that Takebe had been seeking thirteen years earlier, in 1722 (Fig. 2.11). It is truly astounding that this formula was discovered first in Japan, despite the fact it did not possess the theories of infinity or calculus.

Takebe is said to have stared at the several tens of decimal places that he worked out in order to calculate circle-related values such as π or the length of an arc. He encouraged his students with the words, "There is good when obeying the soul of mathematics and suffering when not," and there can be no doubt that Takebe himself had similar feelings when studying the circle. He went on to say, "If we follow this, acknowledging that we will obtain a solution even before we understand [the problem], we are surely at peace. We suffer and are daunted because we feel doubt. Because we suffer and are daunted, it is difficult to obtain [a solution]. We feel doubt, not knowing if we will be able to obtain [a solution] or if we understand [the problem]." I do not know of any other mathematician from any other time or place who has described their work using words such as "soul." This has led me to think that Takebe's mathematics should be called "the way of mathematics." The term "way" is used in Japan in relation to artistic pursuits such as the tea ceremony, flower arrangement, and appreciation of incense, where it means the search for beauty and balance through rational thinking. Such pursuits do not attempt to apply themselves to something useful. Rather they are mental activities through which people try to improve themselves to some degree. It was likely the same for Takebe. By confronting numbers as well as himself, Takebe was able to discover the laws that lay behind those numbers.

It was only natural that the Tokugawa shoguns should have

valued his abilities highly. He served both the sixth and seventh shoguns and was set to retire when Yoshimune succeeded as the eighth and called him back to his service to revise the calendar. Means of measurement and a calendar are essential for the management of groups and organizations, and they explain why mathematicians have always been valued by those in power. They do not only think of abstract theories but also apply their knowledge and ability in practical ways. Takebe acted as an adviser on astronomy and calendars for Yoshimune and wrote a number of books on these subjects, including *Sanreki zakkō* [Various Considerations on Mathematics and the Calendar], *Kyokusei sokusan gukō* [Humble Considerations of the Observation and the Calculation of the Polestar], and *Jujireki gikai* [Commentary on the Time Granting Calendar]. It was extraordinarily rare for one person to have served three generations of shoguns, and this shows how important a person Takebe was in his society.

Matsunaga Yoshisuke and his 52 digits

Though Takebe's theory was internationally advanced at the time, the number of digits of π he found was not a world record.

Around half a century earlier, when Muramatsu calculated π to seven decimal places, a German–Dutch mathematician, Ludolph van Ceulen (1540–1610) calculated it to 35 decimal places using the perimeter of a regular 32,212,254,720-sided (!) polygon. This is called Ludolph's number after him. Mathematicians in Europe went on to discover various evaluating formulas, rather than just making calculations based on bigger and bigger polygons. One such was the infinite series known as the Gregory–Leibniz series, which was discovered separately by the Scottish mathematician James Gregory (1638–1675) in 1671 and by Leibniz in 1674 (Fig. 2.12). In 1699, the English mathematician Abraham Sharp (1653–1742) obtained π to 72 decimal places by substituting the value $x = 1/\sqrt{3}$ into that series. Then, in 1719, the Frenchman Thomas Fantet de Lagny (1660–1734) calculated π to 127 decimal places using the same method as that

---

Gregory–Leibniz series

$$\arctan x = x - \frac{x^3}{3} + \frac{x^5}{5} - \frac{x^7}{7} + \frac{x^9}{9} - \frac{x^{11}}{11} + \cdots$$

Figure 2.12

of Sharp. Three years later, Takebe announced a way to calculate it to 41 decimal places in his *Tetsujutsu sankei*.

The calculation of π in Japan continued to develop after Takebe; 41 decimal places was not the Japanese record in the Edo period. In the same way that Seki's record was broken by his successor, Takebe, Takebe's record was outdone by his student, Matsunaga Yoshisuke (1690?–1744). During his heyday as a *wasan* mathematician, the theory of the circle continued to develop and expansion formulas for trigonometric functions were obtained. These formulas appear in Matsunaga's *Hōen sankei* [Mathematics of Circles and Squares] of 1739, the year of Takebe's death. They included the one that Euler discovered thirteen years after Takebe. Matsunaga took π to 52 decimal places, eleven more than Takebe. This, a record for the Edo period, occurred around 130 years before the Meiji Restoration of 1868, which led to an influx of Western culture and learning that brought about the decline of *wasan*.

CHAPTER
Three

Wasan, alive today

No reports regarding the calculation of π after Takebe and Matsunaga are known to us; however, the development of *wasan* in general did not stop. Japanese mathematicians continued to explore the world of *wasan* until the Meiji Restoration of 1868.

The previous chapters looked at how *wasan* developed as its mathematicians pursued the cutting edge in mathematics but academic progress is more than that. For example, in the world of sports, development is driven by two spurs: the strengthening of the top teams and the spread of this strength among the others. Similarly, the lateral spread of learning is important. This lateral spread is *wasan*'s specialty. All countries have large numbers of mathematicians who study the latest theories, but there is probably no one studying it on a daily basis as much as it was done during the Edo period in Japan. *Wasan* produced world-class mathematicians like Seki Takakazu and Takebe Katahiro, but its main achievement was that it raised the level of mathematics. It was because of the large numbers of people competing in the field that Japan was able to produce top "mathemetical athletes" who were able to compete with other athletes from throughout the world, even though the country was not exposed to information from the rest of the world.

What is the situation in Japan today? The level of mathematics is certainly not low. There are many excellent mathematicians in Japan who are acknowledged around the world, and Japanese high school students generally perform well in competitions such as the International Mathematical Olympiad (IMO). However, it is doubtful whether there is a sufficient support system in place. In sports, considerable efforts are put into improving the representative team that contains only a handful of elite players, but it seems that hardly any attention is paid to spreading interest and increasing the number of competitors. A case that can be considered is in fencing, where Ōta Yūki received a silver medal at the Beijing Olympics. Strengthening the top level players does lead to some popularization. The silver medal obtained in fencing will possibly increase awareness and lead to increased participation in a sport that has previously attracted little interest among Japanese people. Many children probably look up to Ōta and think they would like to give fencing a try.

However, mathematics rarely gets visibility in the broader society, even when leading scholars publish pioneering work.

This may be reported in the media but such is the nature of mathematics that the general public does not understand it.

The bane of entrance exams

About ten years ago, Japanese newspapers widely reported a news item from overseas that the Poincaré conjecture had finally been solved. The Poincaré conjecture is one of seven Millennium Prize Problems established by the Clay Mathematics Institute of Cambridge, Massachusetts, announced in Paris in 2000. A prize of $1 million was offered for the solution of each of the problems. This gives a good idea of their difficulty. The Poincaré conjecture had been formulated by the French mathematician Henri Poincaré in 1904 but it remained unsolved for nearly one hundred years. It was finally solved in 2003 by the Russian mathematician Grigori Yakovlevich Perelman. In 2006, he was offered the Fields Medal, considered to be the Nobel Prize of mathematics, for his work, but to everyone's surprise, he refused to accept it. (He also refused to accept the Millennium Prize offered by the Clay Mathematics Institute in 2010.) This caused quite a stir at the time. Although there would have been people, seeing this news, who simply thought that some mathematicians were just odd, I doubt there were many who understood the Poincaré conjecture itself. The only thing that remains is the impression that mathematicians are strange, and their greatness does not come across at all. This attitude does not encourage children to aspire to be mathematicians.

No one is going to aspire to participate in the IMO based on newspaper articles alone. Articles mention only the number of medals awarded, without giving any clue about the type of problems for which a solution was provided. Medalists tend to be from renowned private high schools, which get their students into the University of Tokyo. The impression that is created is that most of them are clever students who can study well for exams, rather than that they are high school students who are good at mathematics. No doubt, many children think that they cannot succeed in the world of mathematics unless they get through the difficult hurdle of an entrance exam. In fact, rather than it becoming something for them to aim at, they will likely want to steer well clear of mathematics. It just does not seem like any fun.

Most people probably felt that mathematics was fun at some point during primary school. Children can play happily with numbers, just as with toys, and enjoy the experience. That feeling, however, is lost as children go through secondary school because for children in Japan nowadays, studying is something standard, and all pupils, from the youngest to teenagers, studied together in the same space. What they were studying, though, would have been different. Some would have been practicing calligraphy in one part of the room, while others were using the abacus in another part. One teacher taught everything, so the teacher must have been incredibly busy. It was impossible to keep an eye on everyone, so there would have been children just wandering around. If a modern-day school were like this, there would be panic, with parents claiming that the class was a mess. However, this was in no way a mess. What is important is that children went to the *terakoya* on their own accord even though there was no compulsory education system or entrance exam to study for. They did not need to go if they did not like it, so they must have enjoyed studying there. Even if some children misbehaved, it was completely different from the classroom disturbances seen in modern-day schools. Children seemed to actively study by themselves in a lively atmosphere. At the very least, with respect to mathematics, it is clear that many children wanted to study much more proactively than they do now.

Children in the Edo period did not learn arithmetic only in *terakoya*. In towns, there were also *juku* (specialist private schools) that taught mathematics. They were in such great demand that even just a sign outside the door attracted a queue of people wanting to get in. Even if children attended *terakoya* through a sense of responsibility, though they might not like it, there was no way they would then also go to a mathematics *juku*. They were so popular that even people who were not well-grounded in mathematics would open them as a business. We have seen in Chapter 1 how Yoshida Mitsuyoshi found this situation irritating and formulated *idai* in his *Jinkōki* to test the abilities of teachers. Such *juku* played a bigger role than the *terakoya* in spreading *wasan*. There would have been many *terakoya* in large cities such as Edo or Osaka, but not necessarily in the countryside. There were however mathematics *juku* and teachers even there. This allowed for the lateral development of *wasan*. Behind this development were itinerant mathematicians (*yūreki sanka*) living very different lives from mathematicians of today. They traveled the country teaching mathematics wherever they went. While people like Seki and Takebe developed *wasan* in a linear fashion, from master to licensed student, there were also Japanese mathematicians who worked to develop it laterally.

Yamaguchi Kazu and Chiba Tanehide

One well-known itinerant mathematician was Yamaguchi Kazu (??–1850). He was born in Suibara in Echigo Province (now Agano in Niigata Prefecture) and he liked arithmetic ever since he was a child. Having learned that the *wasan* mathematician Hasegawa Hiroshi (1782–1838), also from Suibara, had opened an arithmetic school in the Kanda district of Edo, he eventually became a student there. The Hasegawa *juku* was dominant among the Seki schools in the latter part of the Edo period. The artist and printmaker Katsushika Hokusai (1760–1849) is said to have studied there too.

Yamaguchi studied at the Hasegawa *juku* for seventeen years and received a license as the seventh-generation successor of Seki, and he continued there as an instructor for a time. In 1817, he decided to teach arithmetic to people throughout the country and over the next twelve years made six long trips, from Mutsu (Aomori) in the north to Hizen (Nagasaki) in the south. He was welcomed everywhere he went as a great mathematics teacher who had come all the way from Edo. Village headmen had him stay at their homes and learned mathematics themselves to such an extent that they set up their own *juku* in the villages to teach local people. This is a bit like music venues for artists stopping en route during a national tour. It shows just how keen for knowledge the people were at that time and how they treated mathematics as entertainment. An infrastructure for mathematics was thus established, and its culture remained in various areas long after the itinerant mathematician had left. It seems Yamaguchi was so popular that the locals tried to prevent him from leaving.

In 1818, Yamaguchi arrived at Matsushima in Sendai. Here, he met Chiba Tanehide (1775–1849), a *wasan* mathematician from Ichinoseki in what is today Iwate Prefecture. Chiba was also a famous itinerant mathematician, with around three thousand students throughout Japan. Hearing of Chiba's reputation, Yamaguchi visited him and began a dialogue (*mondō*), a series of questions and answers concerning mathematics. Inevitably Yamaguchi, a licensed instructor of the Seki school of mathematics, prevailed. Chiba immediately realized how great the gap was in their abilities and he became Yamaguchi's student. This is one thing for a young person, but Chiba was already 44 years old at the time. Considering he already had so many students himself, it would have taken quite a strong personality to study under someone who had beaten him in a test of knowledge. The episode is indicative of the determination that marked the Edo period and of how *wasan* was something that could be referred to as a "way."

Chiba went on to study at the Hasegawa *juku* in Edo and became proficient in the Seki-ryū school of mathematics. He then returned home and taught many students, making the region of Ichinoseki the nation's leading center of *wasan* in the late Edo period. Even now, *wasan* is one of the selling points of the area. The Ichinoseki museum always has various materials on display in the *wasan* corner, and it is also possible to see beautifully colored *sangaku* there. It is quite possibly that this is the only museum that introduces *wasan* in much detail, and a visit there makes it apparent just how much the people of the Edo period enjoyed mathematics.

Chiba did not work to spread arithmetic just in Ichinoseki. His *Sanpō shinsho* [New Mathematics], written in 1830, became a national bestseller in Japan as an advanced textbook that enabled self-study. It is a large work made up of an introductory volume and a further five volumes, and editions continued to be published into the late nineteenth century, even after the Meiji Restoration. It starts with methods of counting and the basics of the abacus, just like the *Jinkōki*, two hundred years earlier. By this time, though, the level of mathematics had risen throughout society, and people increasingly felt that the *Jinkōki* did not challenge them enough. Given this situation, Chiba explained even *enri* (*wasan* analysis), said to be *wasan*'s highest achievement, so that readers could study it without a teacher. Moreover, he also publicized secrets from the Seki-ryū school of mathematics that had never been disclosed and was criticized by conservative *wasan* mathematicians for doing so. In any event, there is no doubt that Chiba Tanehide played an important role in the late period of *wasan*. Despite his background, his achievements in mathematics were later acknowledged and he became a samurai of the Ichinoseki domain and was appointed as a mathematics instructor. Many of those he taught were from the peasant class. During this time, an intellectual culture developed among farmers in northern Japan, and in that sense too, Chiba extended *wasan* laterally in a big way.

Other streams of *wasan*

Both Yamaguchi and Chiba studied in the Hasegawa *juku*, i.e., the dominant branch of the Seki-ryū *wasan* tradition, but other schools also existed. While the Seki-ryū was undeniably the most authoritative form of *wasan*, there were many excellent Japanese mathematicians in competing schools. Among those deserving special mention are Ajima Naonobu (1732–1798) and Aida Yasuaki (1747–1817). They were both from Yamagata

Wasan, alive today

Prefecture, as I am, but I am in no way biased toward them because of our common heritage. They were both highly regarded in their time, and Ajima, in particular, was considered to be on a par with Seki Takakazu, the two being referred to as the twin pillars of *wasan*.

Ajima flourished from the mid to the late eighteenth century, subsequent to Matsunaga Yoshisuke, who calculated π to 52 digits, and prior to Yamaguchi and Chiba. Although he later became a student of the Seki-ryū mathematician Yamaji Nushizumi (1704–1772), he originally started learning mathematics under Irie Masatada, a mathematician of the Nakanishi-ryū. The Nakanishi school had begun with Nakanishi Masayoshi, a *wasan* mathematician who incorporated the traditions of Imamura Chisho, one of the "three sons of Mōri" (see Chapter 1). Seki Takakazu was similarly a student of Takahara Yoshitane, also one of Mōri's "sons." This indicates the point of departure between the different schools.

Ajima was an original scholar who has even been called the progenitor of the *wasan* revival. His *Fukyū sanpō* [Masterpieces of Mathematics] (1799), a collection of papers published posthumously by Kusaka Makoto (1764–1839), explains the concept of logarithms. Ajima himself used the expression *haisū*, literally "distributed numbers," and he invented a way of creating a logarithm table based on the logarithmic characteristic that log xy = log x + log y. For calculating π, he used his own unique method different from that of Seki or Takebe. By discovering the infinite series expansion of $(1 - x)$ to the power $1/n$ and constructing a type of double integral, *wasan* succeeded in determining π from the area (not the circumference) of a circle. Ajima applies this theory to solve many problems.

Ajima has become well-known globally as a result of the discovery of the theorem known as the Ajima–Malfatti theorem. He discovered that when three circles inscribed in a triangle circumscribe each other, the three straight lines that join the points of contact and the points of the triangle cross at one point (Fig. 3.1).

The Italian mathematician, Gian Francesco Malfatti, discussed this theorem in 1803, five years after the death of Ajima. If you consider that the Seki–Bernoulli formula is not known by that name, Ajima is fortunate that his name is included in the name of this theorem. Incidentally, the crater Naonobu on the surface of the moon is named after him.

Ajima not only pursued his own studies, but also nurtured many students, such as Sakabe Kōhan (1759–1824), Kusaka Makoto, and Baba Seitoku (1777–1843). Prominent mathematicians from the last days of the Tokugawa shogunate included

Ajima–Malfatti theorem

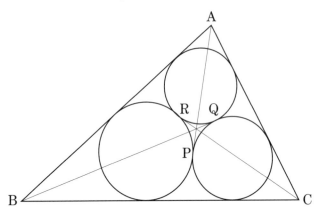

Figure 3.1

Uchida Itsumi (1805–1882, a student of Kusaka's), Hōdōji Zen (1820–1868), and Kuwamoto Masaaki (1830–1863), all Uchida's students.

The other *wasan* mathematician from Yamagata Prefecture, Aida Yasuaki, was born in 1747; only 15 years younger than Ajima, he was basically of the same generation. Aida's arithmetical ability was acknowledged from childhood, and he studied the same Nakanishi-ryū style as Ajima. At the age of 23, he went to Edo to work for the government as an engineer working on irrigation schemes. However, when he was 40, he lost his position when there was a change in government, and he devoted the remainder of his life to mathematics. He founded a school of mathematics called the Saijō-ryū, written with the same ideographs as the Mogami River, a major river in Yamagata Prefecture. He had initially planned to study under Fujita Sadasuke (1734–1807), a famous Seki-ryū mathematician, but something happened that changed his mind after he had applied to the school. One theory is that Fujita found mistakes in Aida's *sangaku* and wanted them fixed before admitting him, but Aida did not agree. It is unclear as to how genuine this story is, but from this point onwards, relations between Aida and the Seki school deteriorated. His *Kaisei sanpō* [Reformed Mathematical Methods] (1785) criticized Fujita's *Seiyō sanpō* [Exact Mathematics]. The dispute with the Seki school, which was an argument rather than a slanderous, mud-slinging campaign, lasted for more than twenty years and Aida's Saijō-ryū was launched in response.

Aida contributed to the spread of *wasan* by improving numerical symbols and providing a commentary related to mathematical concepts. He wrote nearly 600 books while he was alive. Now, many of them are held as part of the Sakuma archive in the Yamagata University Library. Of those, the most important is *Sanpō tenseihō shinan* [Mathematical Introduction to the Tensei Method], a summary of his work in 200 volumes. The

would have produced even more results and astonished people in the West as a unique mathematical system very different from any other system anywhere in the world. Just as judo became known internationally, perhaps "*Wasan*" schools may have been established in various countries across the world. I am sure that I am not the only one who can imagine a world like that.

However, the flow of history put an end to *wasan*. It hardly needs saying that it was the policy of isolation that led to the unique development of Japanese arithmetic during the Edo period. Mathematical information was not brought to Japan from Europe, and information did not reach there from Japan either, with the result that mathematics in the Japanese archipelago advanced in a truly unique way, just like the animals that Darwin studied on the Galapágos Islands.

The Perry Expedition of 1852–1854 had a massive impact on how things subsequently developed since it ultimately led to the opening of Japan to foreign intercourse. This event, which forced Japan to modernize, was also a turning point for *wasan*. An education system is important for modern states, since it is related to what is fundamental in society. If the social system changes, then naturally the education system will also change. The new Meiji government that came into power in 1868 ended the isolation policy and pushed forward a large number of

Wasan, alive today

reforms, and in 1872 established an education system that made elementary school compulsory. The Educational Order issued by the Council of State contained the famous sentence that epitomized the spirit of the reforms: "Let no family of a village and no member of a family be without education." It was then that the essential framework of Japan's modern education system, comprising primary, secondary, and tertiary education, that exists in Japan today was determined.

What sort of education was provided? Various curricula were created, but with respect to mathematics, the authorities initially planned to teach *wasan* in schools. *Wasan* had already become an academic subject across the country, as we have seen, and its level was very high, so it was natural that the new government intended to use it to promote mathematical education, ordering textbooks to be compiled by *wasan* mathematicians. That plan however fell by the wayside; such was the degree of Westernization in government policy that Western mathematics (*yōsan*) was introduced into education. This decision inevitably brought an end to 250 years of *wasan*.

Wasan mathematicians and the introduction of the Gregorian calendar

Even so, *wasan* was not downplayed during the Meiji Restoration. *Wasan* mathematicians played an important role during this time of great change. One area in which they played a significant part was the calendar. Japan had used the traditional lunisolar calendar until then but switched to the widely used Gregorian calendar in 1873. Incidentally, the final day of the lunisolar calendar was the same day as the start of the new educational system, December 3, 1872, which became the first day of the Gregorian calendar, January 1, 1873. December was thus only three days long! Whether or not the temple bells rang out 108 times to welcome in the New Year that year is uncertain.

It goes without saying that a calendar requires the involvement of mathematicians. Though it had been decided that Western mathematics was to be introduced, there were no "Western mathematicians." It was, of course, the *wasan* mathematicians, in particular Uchida Itsumi, one of the students of Ajima Naonobu, who played a central role in the work of creating the new calendar. Uchida was born in Edo in 1805 and entered a Seki-ryū school at the age of eleven, receiving his license to teach at the age of eighteen. He then established a private school teaching *wasan* that he called "Matemateka-juku," the "school of mathematics." This derives from the Latin *mathematica*. Uchida had studied the calendar under the Buddhist priest Entsū (1754–1834), founder of the *bonreki* movement, which sought to spread Indian methods of calendar making, and "Dutch studies" (*rangaku*) under Takano Chōei (1804–1850), thus gathering to himself a broad range of knowledge and training. In 1834, he measured the height of Mount Fuji (3776 m) as 3,475.7 m using a quadrant and a barometer. As a mathematician, his best-known achievement is the discovery of the so-called Soddy's hexlet theorem, long before it was published by a Western mathematician. As Figure 3.2 indicates, the theorem states that when there are spheres A and B inscribed within a sphere O that are circumscribed, there can only be six spheres in a row that circumscribe spheres A and B and are inscribed in sphere O.

The theorem was first published in the West in 1936 by Frederick Soddy (1877–1956), who received the Nobel Prize in Chemistry in 1921 for his research on radioactive decay and isotopes. More than a century earlier, in 1822, Uchida had dedi-

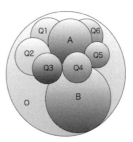

Figure 3.2 Soddy's hexlet theorem

cated a *sangaku* with the theorem on it to the Samukawa Shrine in Kanagawa Prefecture. This means that there is an Edo period *sangaku* containing a pioneering discovery on a global level.

During the Edo period, an official astronomer called the *ten-monkata* devised the annual calendar. The Meiji government initially passed the responsibility for calendars to the Bureau of Astronomy and Calendrical Science, and then to the Calendrical Office (Tenmonkyoku) within the Ministry of Education, which Uchida headed. In 1872, it was decided to substitute the lunisolar one with the Western solar calendar. The success of this calendar reform may be considered the fruit of the power of *wasan*.

Fukuda Riken and the introduction of Western mathematics

The *wasan* mathematician Fukuda Riken (1815–1889) was a junior colleague of Uchida at the Calendrical Office. He established Japan's first mathematical society. He and his elder brother Kintō had studied Saijō-ryū *wasan* and also the calendar at a *juku* in Kyoto. They opened their Juntendō juku in 1834, where they taught *wasan* and surveying. In 1856, Riken published a book on surveying, *Sokuryō shūsei*, in which he wrote

"Astronomy and surveying are necessary for governing and the military." This was three years after Perry's arrival, and the content of the book was highly cognizant of national security, recommending for example the development of surveying devices to give information about the size and armaments of warships. The following year, he published *Seisan sokuchi* [A Short Course in Western Arithmetic], the first work to describe Western-style mathematics. The astronomer Koide Kanemasa (1797–1865), under whom Fukuda had studied, introduced a wealth of Western knowledge through Dutch works. Fukuda had learned of the existence of Western mathematics from Koide, but as he was not familiar with Dutch, he used a Chinese translation to write *Seisan sokuchi*. He used kanji numerals rather than Arabic numerals in his book, and he did not use operators such as + or −. It apparently received some ridicule as "half-Western mathematics." However, at the time, the import of Western books was still forbidden under the national isolation policy, and so it is possible he did not dare to use them.

A second textbook on Western mathematics, *Yōsan yōhō* [Introduction to Western Mathematics], was published slightly later the same year by Yanagawa Shunsan (1832–1870). It introduced numbers and symbols in formats similar to what we see today. Yanagawa was not a mathematician but a scholar of

Western learning who liked mathematics. These two texts on Western mathematics published around the same time, one using kanji numerals and the other Arabic numerals, give a sense of the historical flow from *wasan* to Western mathematics and the tension surrounding it.

Following the Meiji Restoration, Fukuda was called by the new government to work in the Calendrical Office under Uchida. He left this position in 1871, when it was decided to introduce the Gregorian calendar. Six years later, in 1877, he established the Tokyo Sugaku Kaisha (Tokyo Mathematical Society), the first academic society formed in Japan and the forerunner of both the Mathematical Society of Japan and the Physical Society of Japan. Most of the *wasan* mathematicians actively participated in the Society, and it attracted officers from the army and navy, as well as Kikuchi Dairoku (1855–1917), who graduated in mathematics from Cambridge University in 1877 and became a mathematics professor at the University of Tokyo upon his return. The latent power of *wasan* can be felt from the fact that even though the Tokyo Mathematical Society was a private organization, it was able to attract such people. It developed as the premier facility for mathematical research.

It might appear from the above that Fukuda was keen to move from *wasan* to Western mathematics, given how he published

Wasan, alive today

an introduction to Western mathematics and established the first academic society. In reality though, he always worked with Western mathematics as a *wasan* mathematician. Even after the education system was promulgated, *wasan* and Western mathematics co-existed within the Tokyo Mathematical Society. Fukuda wrote in the *Hissan tsūsho* [Complete Work on Arithmetic] published in 1875, two years before the formation of the Society, that: "Both *wasan* and Western mathematics are theories of numbers, so there is no superiority." He had studied Western mathematics comparatively early and was aware that it sought the same things as *wasan*. He had seen the true nature of mathematics as a leading *wasan* mathematician.

Wasan and the development of Western mathematics in Japan

As far as mathematics was concerned, the Meiji Restoration did not simply mean that *wasan* was abandoned and Western mathematics was introduced. *Wasan* certainly fell into abeyance but without the foundation it had built, the introduction of Western mathematics would certainly not have materialized smoothly. If we recall that it was *wasan* mathematicians who were involved in writing textbooks for Western mathematics, it is not an over-statement to say that there would have been no Western mathematics in Japan without *wasan*.

Western mathematics was first taught at the Nagasaki Naval School in 1855. Instruction was given by Dutch naval officers initially for Dutch language and mathematics. A grounding in *wasan* was said to have helped here. For example, one of the trainees was Ono Tomogorō (1817–1898), who had previously studied at the Hasegawa Mathematics School. He apparently mastered the quadratic equations, logarithms, trigonometry, and calculus taught by the Dutch in a very short time. In 1860, he went to the United States as a navigator aboard the *Kanrin Maru*, which was under the command of Katsu Kaishū (1823–1899). *Wasan* mathematicians who lived through the changes that marked the transition from the Edo to the Meiji period, like Uchida Itsumi and Fukuda Riken, made a great contribution to building the foundations of the new government. In fact its success can be said to owe much to the very existence of *wasan* and its two and a half century history from the *Jinkōki* and the achievements of Seki Takakazu. How ironic that *wasan* showed its greatest worth as it ended. Nevertheless, *wasan* did not com-pletely disappear with the introduction of Western mathematics into the school curriculum. *Wasan* mathematicians from

Wasan, alive today

across Japan continued to study it using their own methods and continued to dedicate *sangaku*. The last known dedication of a *sangaku* took place in 1920. The fact that the tradition of *wasan* continued, albeit in a small way, must be due to its lateral, rather than linear, development.

Takahashi Tsumitane, the last *wasan* mathematician

Wasan continued to have a stronghold in the Tōhoku region of northern Japan, partly due to Chiba Tanehide having come from Ichinoseki. The person regarded as the last *wasan* mathematician was also from this region. He was Takahashi Tsumitane from Shiraishi in Miyagi Prefecture (Fig. 3.3). He succeeded to the headship of the Saijō-ryū that Aida Yasuaki created. The fact that the last *wasan* mathematician was born in a farming family is also redolent of *wasan*. The young Takahashi went all the way to a *terakoya* in Yamagata Prefecture to study mathematics, and did not help at the farm even during busy times. His family, which needed all the help they could get, complained quite a lot, but even so, Takahashi could not bring himself to stop studying. This is unimaginable in a modern Japanese family, entangled in tackling children's entrance exams. Mothers nag their primary school children to study hard to get into a good secondary school and eventually to a good university and send them to cram schools three or four times a week. Fathers on the other hand often seem to think that the children do not need to be forced to study that much, but they do not tend to voice their thoughts. At the very least, there are unlikely to be any parents who would order their chil-

Figure 3.3 Takahashi Tsumitane, of the Saijō-ryu school, the last *wasan* mathematician

dren, if they wanted to go to a cram school, to stay and help at home if they had that much time to spare.

My feeling is that study and learning are not things done to order. Learning is something that has its own appeal and we do it because we cannot help it, even if ordered to stop by parents. It is because we like it so much that we challenge ourselves, and so continuously acquire the knowledge and understanding that lead to great accomplishment. Studying because parents order it, without any wish to do so, is simply a method for passing entrance exams, and what has been learned is instantly forgotten when the exams are over. It is a shame, since mathematics studied through the love of it is life-enrichening.

Wasan from the Edo period was like that. Mathematics in Japan was not something to be useful but more something to learn because it was fun. In that respect, too, Takahashi can be said to have developed like a typical *wasan* mathematician. On his death, he left an item with the message that it must not be opened for one hundred years. It was finally made public a few years ago (Fig. 3.4). It is as though the hand-written calculations and magic squares from over a century ago are bringing the beauty of *wasan* to the modern world. It is full of the spirit of enjoying mathematics in a pure way.

Loving and hating mathematics, two sides of the same coin

For the modern Japanese, mathematics is basically Western mathematics. This is obviously going to be the case, as it is the only mathematics taught in Japanese schools. Moreover, many people have the image of it as an academic subject brought in from the West and that it is something that would not have existed in Japan without the policy of aggressive modernization that followed the Meiji Restoration. That is to be expected, given that they have only ever seen equations using the alphabet and unfamiliar symbols. However, as we have seen here, this does not mean that the Japanese did not have the capability of creating mathematics. People of the past developed their own mathematics with their own hands and heads and discovered numerous formulas and theorems earlier than in the West. Even people living in farming villages enjoyed mathematics and

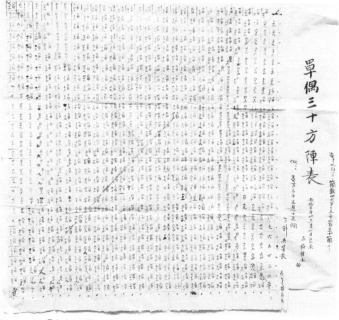

Figure 3.4 Takahashi Tsumitane's magic square (created in 1902)

Wasan, alive today

I believe that Edo period Japan had a greater mathematical sense than any other country in the world.

Western mathematics has been developing its status as an internationally common language. I would not deny that and Japanese people should learn it and become familiar with it. However, it is up to us to brush it up to create our own new and unique world. *Wasan* mathematicians of the Edo period caught up with China's mathematicians and took it further. There is no reason why a modern-day Japanese person could not do the same thing.

Many people seem to dislike mathematics these days. However, my theory is that "dislike" is the flip side of "like." People do not even get to the point of disliking something that they have no interest in at all. Therefore, those who say that they dislike mathematics in fact are probably intrigued by it. If anything, they want to be able to say they like it. During the Edo period, there was an atmosphere prevailing that somehow led naturally from that type of interest in mathematics to actually liking it. This was possible because of the way people approached the fascination of academic subjects. They thought of mathematics not as a means to succeed in exams but as something to be enjoyed as an end in itself. By following suit, modern-day Japanese people should be able to enjoy mathematics just as the children of the *terakoya* did.

Exercises

Crane-tortoise calculation
(*tsurukame-zan*)

鶴
亀
算

There are several cranes and tortoises.
They have a total of 100 heads and 272 legs.
How many cranes and tortoises are there?

From the *Sanpō tenzan shinanroku*
[Guide to the Algebraic Method of Geometry] (1815)

The crane-tortoise calculation first appeared in the *Sunzi suanjing*, a Chinese work of the fourth century. There the animals were pheasants and rabbits rather than cranes and tortoises; this change apparently happened in 1815, in Sakabe Kōhan's *Sanpō tenzan shinanroku*. Interestingly enough, the solution given below [crane: (4a − b)/2 birds] had earlier been passed down as a song: "The solution for the cranes is obtained by multiplying the number of heads by four, removing the number of legs, and dividing by two."

SOLUTION

This problem is easily solved by setting up simultaneous equations.

Let the number of cranes be x, and let the number of tortoises be y.

Total number of heads: $x + y = 100$ ······①

Total number of legs: $2x + 4y = 272$ ······②

If y is removed by performing ① x 4 − ②,

$$
\begin{aligned}
4x + 4y &= 400 \\
-)\ 2x + 4y &= 272 \\
\hline
2x &= 128 \\
x &= 64 \quad \text{······③}
\end{aligned}
$$

From ① and ③,

$$
\begin{aligned}
y &= 100 - 64 \\
&= 36,
\end{aligned}
$$

which is the number of cranes.

Generally, if the total number of heads is taken to be a and the total number of legs is taken to be b, the simultaneous equations are

The total number of heads: $x + y = a$

The total number of legs: $2x + 4y = b$

Exercises

If this is solved in a way similar to the above, then

$x = (4a - b)/2$

$y = (b - 2a)/2$

is obtained.

Cranes: $(4a - b)/2$

Tortoises: $(b - 2a)/2$

This solution can be found mechanically thanks to the power of algebra, using variables such as x and y, but how can we solve this without algebra?

We can do it by thinking of the number of legs in terms of an area.

If the length is taken to be the number of heads and the breadth is taken to be the number of legs per crane or tortoise, then length × breadth = number of legs.

This can be seen clearly if drawn on a diagram. The rectangles on the left and right in Fig. 4.1a represent the total number of tortoise and crane legs respectively. The area of the combined L-shape is equivalent to the total number of legs, which is 272.

$\ggg\ggg$

鶴
亀
算

>>>>>

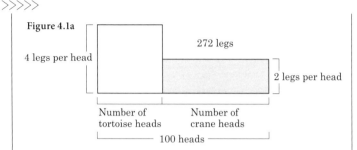

Figure 4.1a

4 legs per head

272 legs

2 legs per head

Number of
tortoise heads

Number of
crane heads

100 heads

Figure 4.1b

Number of
tortoise heads

2 legs per head

272-200
=72 legs

200 legs

2 legs per head

100 heads

Let us divide this L-shaped figure into a rectangle
above and below (Fig. 4.1b). Since the lower rectangle
is $100 \times 2 = 200$ (length x breadth), the upper rectangle
must be $272 - 200 = 72$.

This rectangle is the number of tortoise heads $\times 2$, so
the number of tortoise heads $= 72 \div 2 = 36$.

Therefore the number of crane heads $= 100 - 36 = 64$.

Solution: 64 cranes, 36 tortoises

2

The calculation of crows
(*karasu-zan*)

から
す
算

If there are 999 crows on each of 999 beaches, and if each crow caws 999 times, how many caws would there be in total?

From the *Jinkōki*

SOLUTION

The solution is simple. You just need to calculate 999 × 999 × 999. Providing a specific context for a simple practice calculation, however, makes you want to solve it, and the solution becomes more interesting. The beauty of the *Jinkōki* is that  it set innovative questions that made people want to solve arithmetical problems that seem dull at first sight.

>>>>>

>>>>>

If a calculator is used, the solution can be easily calculated as follows.

$$999 \times 999 \times 999 = 998{,}001 \times 999 = 997{,}002{,}999$$

But this is not much fun, so let us be a little more innovative.

First,

$$999 \times 999 = (1{,}000 - 1) \times (1{,}000 - 1)$$
$$= 1{,}000^2 - 2 \times 1{,}000 + (-1) \times (-1)$$
$$= (1{,}000 - 2) \times 1{,}000 + 1$$
$$= 998{,}000 + 1$$
$$= 998{,}001$$

then,

$$998{,}001 \times 999 = 998{,}001 \times (1{,}000 - 1)$$
$$= 998{,}001 \times 1{,}000 - 998{,}001$$
$$= 998{,}001{,}000 - 998{,}001$$
$$= 99{,}7002{,}999$$

This allows the solution to be obtained without the use
of a calculator or abacus.

Solution: 997,002,999 caws

3

旅人算

The calculation of travelers
(*tabibito-zan*)

Person **A** travels from Kyoto to Edo on foot at a pace of 15 and half miles a day. Person **B** travels from Edo to Kyoto on foot at a pace of 24 and half miles a day. They leave on the same day. How far did each of them travel when they met? The distance between Kyoto and Edo is 240 miles.

From the *Sanpō keiko zue taisei*
[Compilation of Mathematical Exercises, Illustrated] (1831)

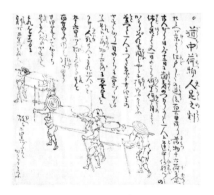

SOLUTION

The people **A** and **B** get closer by 40 miles (15 and a half + 24 and a half) a day.

As the distance between Kyoto and Edo is 240 miles, they meet 6 days later (240 miles ÷ 40 miles/day = 6 days).

Therefore, the distance traveled for 6 days by each is

A: 15.5 (miles/day) × 6 (days) = 93 miles

B: 24.5 (miles/day) × 6 (days) = 147 miles

Solution: They met when **A** had traveled 93 miles and **B** had traveled 147 miles.

4 | Rice bale calculation
(*tawarasugi-zan*)

俵杉算

Rice bales are piled so that there is one at the top, two in the second row, three in the third, and so on. If there are thirteen bales at the bottom, how many bales are there in total?

From the *Jinkōki*

SOLUTION

From the top row, the number of rice bales in order is

1, 2, 3, 4, 5, 6, 7, 8, 9, 10, 11, 12, 13

There are one to thirteen bales, so their total is

$1 + 2 + 3 + 4 + 5 + 6 + 7 + 8 + 9 + 10 + 11 + 12 + 13$

Reversing the order and adding the sum to itself results in

$$
\begin{aligned}
S &= 1 + 2 + 3 + 4 + 5 + 6 + 7 + 8 + 9 + 10 + 11 + 12 + 13 \\
+) S &= 13 + 12 + 11 + 10 + 9 + 8 + 7 + 6 + 5 + 4 + 3 + 2 + 1 \\
\hline
2S &= 14 + 14 + 14 + 14 + 14 + 14 + 14 + 14 + 14 + 14 + 14 + 14 + 14 \\
&= 14 \times 13 \\
S &= \frac{14 \times 13}{2} \\
&= 91
\end{aligned}
$$

In general, we have the following rule:

If we let n be a natural number, then

$$1 + 2 \cdots + n = n\,(n + 1)/2$$

We can set $n = 13$ in this problem.

Solution: 91 bales

5 | Guessing number calculation
(*sassadate*)

30 *go* stones are passed to a friend who lines them up out of your sight.

The rules for lining them up are as follows:

- One or two can be placed down at the same time.
- Whether one or two are placed down at the same time, the friend calls out "here" (*sā*) just once.

The friend starts to place the *go* stones, calling out "here, here" (*sā sā*). If you hear the call-out 18 times before all 30 are placed, how many times was one placed and how many times were two placed?

From the *Kanja otogi zōshi*
[Collection of Interesting Results] (1743)

SOLUTION

If the number of times that one *go* stone is placed is taken to be *x*, then the number of times that two *go* stones are placed is 18 − *x* times. The equation for the total number of *go* stones placed is

$$x \times 1 + (18 - x) \times 2 = 30$$

Solving this gives *x* = 6, so the number of times that one is placed is 6, and the number of times that two are placed is 12.

Generally, if the total number of *go* stones is taken to be a, and the number of call-outs is taken to be n:

$$x \times 1 + (n - x) \times 2 = a$$
$$x + 2n - 2x = a$$
$$x = 2n - a$$

Consequently, the number of times two are placed is

$$n - x = n - (2n - a) = a - n$$

The number of times that one is placed: 2n − a

The number of times that two are placed: a − n

Solution: One is placed down six times and two are placed down 12 times.

---

6 Silk thief calculation
(*kinunusubito-zan*)

Thieves have stolen some lengths of silk and are discussing how to divide their spoils. If they split the silk into 8 *tan* each, there would be 7 *tan* lacking. If they split it into 7 *tan* each, there would be 8 *tan* left. How many thieves were there and what was the amount of silk they stole?

From the *Jinkōki*

SOLUTION

This can also be solved using diagrams, as we did with the crane-tortoise calculation. If the length is the number of thieves, and the breadth is the amount of silk given to each person, then the area of a given rectangle (length × breadth) represents the total amount of silk. Where the silk is split into 8 *tan* each, with 7 *tan* lacking, is shown diagrammatically in Fig. 4.2a. Where the silk is split into

>>>>>

Figure 4.2a

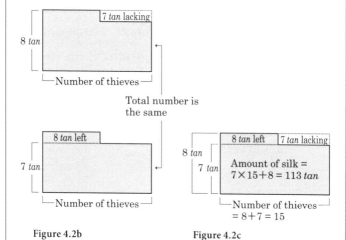

Figure 4.2b

Figure 4.2c

7 *tan* each, with 8 *tan* left, is shown diagrammatically in Fig. 4.2b. This must be the total amount of silk stolen. When the diagrams are superimposed (Fig. 4.2c), we get lengthways the number of thieves, 8 + 7 = 15 and in the area, the amount of silk stolen, 7 × 15 + 8 = 113.

Solution: 15 thieves, 113 *tan*

薬
師
算

7 The Yakushi calculation
(*yakushi-zan*)

A square is formed with 8 *go* stones on each side. None are placed inside the square. One side of 8 stones is left as it is, and the remaining stones are lined up along the other sides. If four stones remain on the left side, how many stones are there in total?

From the *Jinkōki*

The reason this is called the Yakushi calculation is related to the number 12 that appears in the solution. Yakushi is the Buddha of Medicine and he made twelve great vows to cure all illness.

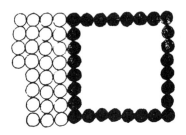

SOLUTION

In actual fact, the number 8 given for a side in the question is not required. Let us explain this using a diagram. Let the number of stones on one side be a, so that there are 4a − 4 stones in total on all the sides of the square. Realign these 4a − 4 stones so that there are stones on each side. In that case, after three lines, there are a few left for the fourth line. This would be (4a − 4) − 3a = a − 4. This is four, so since a − 4 = 4, we see that a = 8. Can you see it? It shows that the problem does not need to provide the information that one side is made up of eight. Therefore, it becomes apparent that there are 4 × 8 − 4 = 28 stones (Fig. 4.3a).

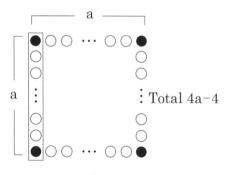

Figure 4.3 a

 Line stones up

Figure 4.3 b

↓ Line stones up

4

a

The stones
remaining
on the left:
$(4a-4)-3a$
$= a-4$

3a in 3 rows

When we review the result, it becomes apparent that there are $(a - 4)$ stones remaining on the left-hand side in Fig. 4.3b, which means that there are $(a - (a - 4)) = 4$ stones at the bottom of the three rows on the right-hand side. That further means that there are always $4 \times 3 = 12$ stones in the part lining the bottom of the square in Fig. 4.3c. The solution can be thus expressed as

>>>>>

>>>>>

Figure 4.3 c

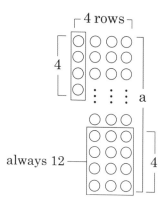

The number of stones = (the number of stones remaining on the left side) × 4 + 12

From this, we get 4 × 4 + 12 = 28.

Solution: 28 stones

Arithmetical restorations
(*mushikui-zan*)

An account book recorded the purchase of rice, but a portion of the record had been eaten by insects. "273 kg of rice was bought for ____ 45 yen, with the price of rice per kg at ___ yen." Fill in each blank box with a digit.

From the *Sangaku keiko daizen*
[A Compendium of Mathematical Practice Problems] (1808)

SOLUTION

$$
\begin{array}{r}
2\ 7\ 3 \\
\times\ ⑤\ ② \\
\hline
\boxed{\ }\ ③\ \boxed{\ }\ ① \\
\boxed{\ }\ ⑥\ \boxed{\ }\ ④ \\
\hline
\boxed{\ }\ ⑦\ \boxed{\ }\ 4\ 5
\end{array}
$$

❶ The ones place in the solution is five, so ① = 5.

❷ The only number that gives a five in the ones place by multiplying it by three is five. ② = 5.

❸ As 273 × ② = 273 × 5 = 1,365, ③ = 136.

❹ Adding ③'s 136's 6 with ④ gives the four in the tens place in the solution.
From 6 + ④ = ⋯ 4, ④ = 8.

❺ Only six gives ④, in other words eight, by multiplying it by three of 273.
⑤ = 6.

❻ From 273 × ⑤ = 273 × 6 = 1,638, ⑥ = 163.

❼ 1,365 + 16,380 = 17,745,
so 273 × 65 = 17,745, giving ⑦ = 177.

Solution: 273 kg of rice was bought for 17,745 yen, at a price of 65 yen per kg.

9

Freight cost calculation
(*unchin-zan*)

運賃算

250 kg of rice is to be transported by ship. The freight cost will be paid in rice. If the freight cost is 7 kg per 100 kg, how much will it cost to transport the 250 kg?

From the *Jinkōki*

SOLUTION

As 7/100 kg is needed per 1 kg for the freight cost, it first seems that $250 \times 7/100$ is needed, but since the rice to cover the cost will be removed before being carried, less than 250 kg will be shipped.

Let us set up an equation taking this point into consideration.

If the cost is x kg, $250 - x$ kg will actually be carried. This gives the following equation.

$$x = (250 - x) \times (7/100)$$
$$(1 + 7/100)\,x = 250 \times (7/100)$$
$$107x = 250 \times 7$$
$$x = 1{,}750/107$$
$$= 16.355140 \cdots$$

Solution: 16.35514 kg

10 105 subtraction
(hyakugozen-zan)

百五減算

The 105 subtraction was a problem originally found in the *Sunzi suanjing*, a Chinese text introduced to Japan in the eighth century. The 105 subtracted repeatedly at the end is the lowest common multiple of seven, five, and three.

Several *go* stones are placed in a bag. They are first removed seven at a time, and when there are fewer than seven in the bag, the number remaining is called out. Next, all the stones are returned to the bag and the process is repeated, next by taking out five stones at a time, then by removing three at a time. If there were two remaining when seven at a time were taken out, one when five at a time were taken out, and two when three at a time were taken out, how many stones were there in the bag at the start?

From the *Jinkōki*

SOLUTION

Let the total number of *go* stones be N, the number of times that seven are taken out be x, with the remainder in that case a, the number of times that five are taken out be y, with the remainder in that case b, and the number of times that three are taken out be z, with the remainder in that case c.

$$N = 7x + a \quad \cdots \textcircled{1}$$
$$N = 5y + b \quad \cdots \textcircled{2}$$
$$N = 3z + c \quad \cdots \textcircled{3}$$

Then,

$$\textcircled{1} \times 15 \qquad 15N = 105x + 15a$$
$$+ \textcircled{2} \times 21 \qquad 21N = 105y + 21b$$
$$+ \textcircled{3} \times 70 \qquad 70N = 210z + 70c$$
$$\overline{\phantom{+ \textcircled{3} \times 70 \qquad } 106N = 105(x + y + 2z) + (15a + 21b + 70c)}$$

$\gg\gg\gg$

>>>>>

This can be rearranged as follows:

$$N = 105(x + y + 2z) + (15a + 21b + 70c) - 105N$$
$$= 105(x + y + 2z - N) + (15a + 21b + 70c)$$
$$= (15a + 21b + 70c) - \underline{105(N - x - y - 2z)}$$
$$= (15a + 21b + 70c) - \underline{105 \times \text{(natural number)}}$$

Therefore, the following calculation should suffice.

Multiply the remainder after taking out 7 by 15 to get

$2 \times 15 = 30$.

Multiply the remainder after taking out 5 by 21 to get

$1 \times 21 = 21$.

Multiply the remainder after taking out 3 by 70 to get

$2 \times 70 = 140$.

The total of all three of these gives $30 + 21 + 140 = 191$.

Next,

105 is subtracted from this before the solution becomes

negative.

$191 - 105 = 86$, and there you have it!

Solution: 86 stones

Names of large numbers, *Jinkōki*

About the Author and Translators

Author: Sakurai Susumu

Born in Yamagata Prefecture in 1968, Sakurai Susumu graduated from the Department of Mathematics and the graduate school at the Tokyo Institute of Technology. He is a science navigator and was a Fellow of the Center for the Study of World Civilizations at the Tokyo Institute of Technology (2007–2013). While studying at university, he taught at cram schools and sought to explain mathematics and physics to students in interesting ways. In doing so, he developed "Science Entertainment," activities that communicate the surprising and inspiring nature of mathematics through human interactions between people and familiar objects. Sakurai lectures all over Japan and has authored books such as *Omoshirokute nemurenakunaru sūgaku* [Mathematics, Too Exciting to Sleep], *Kandō suru sūgaku*, [Inspirational Mathematics], and *Setsugetsuka no sūgaku* [Mathematics of Snow, Moon, and Flowers].

Translator: Emma Ford

Emma Ford has been working as a translator with Ulatus for more than 5 years. She has spent half her life in Japan and the rest in the UK. She studied mathematics at the University of Oxford and worked as a bilingual analyst in Cambridge before becoming a professional translator.

Translation and editorial adviser: Gaynor Sekimori

Gaynor Sekimori has been working as an academic translator and editor for more than thirty years in the fields of cultural, economic and religious history. She obtained her doctorate at the University of Cambridge and worked at the University of Tokyo for six years as researcher in Japanese religious history and Shugendō and as managing editor of the *International Journal of Asian Studies*.

（英文版）**夢中になる！江戸の数学**
Wasan, the Fascination of Traditional Japanese Mathematics

2018年3月27日　第1刷発行

著　者　　桜井 進

訳　者　　エマ・フォード

英訳監修　関守ゲイノー

発行所　　一般財団法人出版文化産業振興財団
　　　　　〒101-0051 東京都千代田区神田神保町3-12-3
　　　　　電話　03-5211-7282(代)

ホームページ　http://www.jpic.or.jp/

印刷・製本所　大日本印刷株式会社